the Southern Review

PUBLISHED QUARTERLY AT LOUISIANA STATE UNIVERSITY

POETRY EDITOR
Jessica Faust-Spitzfaden

FICTION AND NONFICTION EDITOR
Cara Blue Adams

BUSINESS MANAGER
Leslie A. Green

EDITORIAL ASSISTANT
Emily Nemens

Library of Congress Catalog Number 36-25494

Copyright © 2013 by Louisiana State University Press

DESIGNER: Barbara Neely Bourgoyne
TYPEFACE: Adobe Minion Pro
MASTHEAD ILLUSTRATION: *Live Oak* by Barry Moser, 2004. Woodcut.
PRINTER: Data Reproductions

ON THE COVER: *Light Horse (Buck)* by Alison Rossiter, 2006.
Light drawing on gelatin silver paper. 8 x 10 in.

Light drawings by Alison Rossiter appear on pages 87 to 94.
Copyright © Alison Rossiter, courtesy Alison Rossiter and Stephen Bulger Gallery

Periodicals postage paid at Baton Rouge, Louisiana, and at additional mailing offices.

The Southern Review (ISSN 0038-4534) is published quarterly. Individual subscription rates are $40 for one year, $70 for two years, $90 for three years, and $12 for single copies; institutional subscriptions are $75 for one year, $100 for two years, $125 for three years, and $24 for single copies. It is distributed in North America by Ubiquity Distributors, Inc.

The Southern Review is available to subscribers on microfilm from ProQuest (Ann Arbor, Michigan 48106) and on microfiche from Kraus Microform (Millwood, New York 10546-1035). Abstracts of essays and reviews, beginning with volume 4, number 1 (January 1968), through volume 12, number 4 (October 1976), are on file at the Modern Language Association Abstract Office, 62 Fifth Avenue, New York, New York 10011. Articles appearing in this journal are abstracted and indexed in *Humanities International Complete, Book Review Index, EBSCO Publishing, Historical Abstracts,* and/or *America: History and Life, Humanities Index, MLA International Bibliography,* and *Poem Finder.*

The Southern Review is a member of the Council of Literary Magazines and Presses. LSU is an equal opportunity university for both educational and employment purposes. We read unsolicited prose postmarked September 1–December 1 and unsolicited poetry postmarked September 1–February 1. Submissions will not be acknowledged or returned unless accompanied by an SASE. Only previously unpublished works will be considered. Contributions, subscriptions, and advertising matter should be addressed to *The Southern Review.* Postmaster: Send address changes to *The Southern Review,* 3990 W. Lakeshore Drive, LSU, Baton Rouge, Louisiana 70808.

the Southern Review volume 49:1 winter 2013

POETRY

Contributors

IDRIS ANDERSON's first collection of poems, *Mrs. Ramsay's Knee*, was selected by Harold Bloom for the May Swenson Poetry Award. She won a Pushcart Prize in 2010 and a special mention in the 2012 Pushcart anthology. Her poems have appeared in *AGNI*, *The Hudson Review*, and *The Nation*. She recently won the first Arts & Letters Prime award. She was born and grew up in Charleston, South Carolina, and moved to the San Francisco area almost two decades ago.

IAN BASSINGTHWAIGHTE is a writer and photographer living in Boston. He was a Fulbright fellow in fiction to Egypt, where he recently "finished" his first novel. He is now endlessly editing it.

CHARD DENIORD is the author of four books of poetry, *The Double Truth*, *Night Mowing*, *Sharp Golden Thorn*, and *Asleep in the Fire*. He also published a book of essays and interviews with seven senior American poets, *Sad Friends, Drowned Lovers, Stapled Songs: Conversations and Reflections on Twentieth Century American Poets*. He is the cofounder of the New England College MFA program in poetry and a professor of English at Providence College. He lives in Putney, Vermont.

DEBORAH FLANAGAN's work has appeared in *Ploughshares*, *FIELD*, and *The Gettysburg Review*. Her manuscript *Or, Gone* won the 2012 Snowbound Chapbook Poetry Award from Tupelo Press. At the Academy of American Poets, she helped create the Online Poetry Classroom. She lives in the Lower East Side in New York City.

BRENDAN GALVIN is the author of sixteen collections of poems. *Habitat: New and Selected Poems, 1965–2005* was a finalist for the National Book Award. Recent collections include *Ocean Effects* and *Whirl Is King*. His translation of Sophocles's *Women of Trachis* appeared in the Penn Greek Drama Series.

KARL TARO GREENFELD is the author of six books, including the novel *Triburbia* and story collection *NowTrends*. His fiction has appeared in *Harper's*, *The Paris Review*, Best American Short Stories, and PEN/O. Henry Prize Stories.

HENRY HART has published critical studies of Seamus Heaney, Robert Lowell, and Geoffrey Hill, as well as a biography of James Dickey and three books of poetry. He recently completed the manuscript of a fourth collection of poetry, "Orpheus Among Familiar Ghosts." He teaches English at the College of William & Mary, where he is the Mildred and J. B. Hickman Professor of Humanities.

STEVEN HARVEY is the author of three books of personal essays: *A Geometry of Lilies*, *Lost in Translation*, and *Bound for Shady Grove*. He is a professor of English and creative writing at Young Harris College and a member of the nonfiction faculty in the Ashland University MFA program in creative writing. "The Vanishing Point" is a chapter from a memoir called "The Book of Knowledge and Wonder."

KATHERINE HEINY's stories have been published in *The New Yorker*, *Glimmer Train*, and *The Antioch Review*; presented on *Selected Shorts* on NPR; and performed off-Broadway. She lives in Washington, D.C., with her husband and two children.

JOHN KINSELLA's most recent volume of poetry is *Jam Tree Gully*. He is a Fellow of Churchill College, Cambridge University and a Professorial Research Fellow at the University of Western Australia.

LANCE LARSEN, the poet laureate of Utah, has published four collections, most recently *Genius Loci*. His poems and essays appear widely. He has received a number of awards, including a Pushcart Prize and a fellowship from the National Endowment for the Arts. A professor at Brigham Young University, he recently directed a study abroad program in Madrid.

PETER LASALLE is the author of several books of fiction, most recently a novel, *Mariposa's Song*. A new story collection, *What I Found Out About Her*, is forthcoming from University of Notre Dame Press. His fiction has appeared in a number of magazines and anthologies, including *Zoetrope: All Story*, *Tin House*, Best American Short Stories, and PEN/O. Henry Prize Stories. He divides his time between Austin, Texas, and Narragansett in his native Rhode Island.

ANGIE MACRI was born and raised in southern Illinois. Her recent work appears in *Natural Bridge* and *Crazyhorse*. An Arkansas Arts Council fellow, she teaches in Little Rock.

ERIKA MEITNER is the author of *Makeshift Instructions for Vigilant Girls* and *Ideal Cities*, which was a 2009 National Poetry Series winner. Her poems have been published in *The New Republic*, *Virginia Quarterly Review*, and *The American Poetry Review*. She is currently an associate professor of English at Virginia Tech, where she teaches in the MFA program.

JEREDITH MERRIN is the author of two collections of poetry, *Shift* and *Bat Ode*, and a book of criticism, *An Enabling Humility: Marianne Moore, Elizabeth Bishop, and the Uses of Tradition*. Her essays, reviews, and poems have been published in *The Hudson Review*, *The Paris Review*, and *Slate*.

SUSAN LAUGHTER MEYERS is the author of *My Dear, Dear Stagger Grass*, which received the Cider Press Review Editor's Prize and will be published this autumn. Her collection *Keep and Give Away* won the South Carolina Poetry Book Prize. Her poems have appeared recently in *Southern Poetry Review*, *2013 Poet's Market*, and *North Carolina Literary Review*.

DAVID MOOLTEN is a physician specializing in transfusion medicine. He writes and practices in Philadelphia, Pennsylvania. His most recent book of verse, *Primitive Mood*, won the 2009 T. S. Eliot Prize from Truman State University Press.

CHINELO OKPARANTA was born in Port Harcourt, Nigeria. Her stories have appeared or are forthcoming in *Granta*, *The Kenyon Review*, and *The Iowa Review*. She has a collection of stories forthcoming from Granta Books (United Kingdom) and Houghton Mifflin Harcourt (United States). Her debut novel, tentatively titled *Under the Udara Trees*, will shortly follow. A graduate of the Iowa Writers' Workshop, she is currently the Olive B. O'Connor Fellow in Creative Writing at Colgate University.

KEVIN PRUFER is the author of five books of poems, the most recent of which are *In a Beautiful Country* and *National Anthem*, named one of the five best poetry books of 2008 by *Publishers Weekly*. His next book, *Churches*, is forthcoming from Four Way Books. He is editor-at-large of *Pleiades: A Journal of New Writing* and a professor in the creative writing program at the University of Houston.

SUSAN BLACKWELL RAMSEY's book, *A Mind Like This*, won the Prairie Schooner Book Prize for Poetry and was published last September.

THOMAS REITER's most recent book of poems is *Catchment*. He has received grants from the National Endowment for the Arts and the New Jersey State Council on the Arts. His poems have appeared in *Poetry*, *The Georgia Review*, and *The Sewanee Review*.

ALISON ROSSITER studied visual art at the Rochester Institute of Technology and the Banff School of Fine Arts (now the Banff Centre). Her photography can be found in many major collections, including the Art Institute of Chicago, the J. Paul Getty Museum, the San Francisco Museum of Modern Art, and the National Gallery of Canada. Alison lives and works in New Jersey and New York City.

PHILIP SCHULTZ's memoir is *My Dyslexia*. His most recent poetry collection is *The God of Loneliness: Selected and New Poems*, and his collection *Failure* won the 2008 Pulitzer Prize in poetry. He founded and directs The Writers Studio, a private school for poetry and fiction writing in Manhattan, with branches in Tucson, San Francisco, Amsterdam, and online.

CARRIE SHIPERS has published poems in *Crab Orchard Review*, *Hayden's Ferry Review*, and *North American Review*. She is the author of two chapbooks, *Ghost-Writing* and *Rescue Conditions*, and a full-length collection, *Ordinary Mourning*.

AISHA SABATINI SLOAN was born in California. She earned an MA in Cultural Studies and Studio Art from NYU's Gallatin School of Individualized Study, and an MFA in Creative Nonfiction from the University of Arizona. After teaching English composition in Tucson for several years, she lives in Los Angeles, and is training to become a yoga instructor. Her collection of essays, *The Fluency of Light: Coming of Age in a Theater of Black and White*, will be published by the University of Iowa Press this spring.

MAGGIE SMITH is the author of *Lamp of the Body*, *Nesting Dolls*, and *The List of Dangers*. She has received fellowships and awards from the National Endowment for the Arts, the Ohio Arts Council, and the Virginia Center for the Creative Arts. Her poems have appeared in *The Gettysburg Review*, *Shenandoah*, and *The Iowa Review*.

BRIAN SWANN has two books forthcoming: *In Late Night*, from Johns Hopkins University Press, and *Sky Loom: Native American Myth, Story, Song*, from the University of Nebraska Press.

GREG WRENN's first book of poems, *Centaur*, was awarded the 2013 Brittingham Prize and will be published by the University of Wisconsin Press in spring 2013. His work has appeared in *New England Review*, *The American Poetry Review*, and *The Yale Review*. A former Wallace Stegner Fellow in Poetry, he currently is a Jones Lecturer at Stanford University. He was born and raised in Jacksonville, Florida.

DEBORAH FLANAGAN

Plum Perfect

Émile is treated to plum pudding by a stranger named Monsieur de Fontgibu.
Ten years later, he orders plum pudding at a restaurant in Paris.
"*Malheureusement*," replies the waiter, "the last dish was just served to another customer, de Fontgibu."
Twenty years later, once again he orders the pudding, recalling the incident, telling his friends
that only de Fontgibu is missing to make the scene complete.
Just then, de Fontgibu enters the room.

Carl Jung and the ancient Chinese philosophers embrace
yuan: certain people are meant to find each other.
It's why it's impossible for two people to take their eyes off each other.
It takes hundreds of rebirths to bring two people to cross a river in the same ferry,
a hundred years of good deeds to bring two people
to rest their heads on the same pillow.

1

The Map of the Forest

Grief is made of yellow pine, hickory, ash. Stand in the forest of sorrow. *The bereaved must be urged to sit in a sunny room with an open fire.* The fire burns with maple burl; desire is made of pine and cedar, poplar, Sitka spruce. Part of it is red, charting the heart, the other part green with trees. Red means she's leaving; white means she'll return. Green marks the spot. The farthest distance lies between touching and not touching. *The palate rejects the thought of food; digestion is not in the best order.* Her coffin is made of incense cedar and cypress. Your wail is made of birch trees, paperbark unwinding white in the wind. Unwilling to wander, watch the geese fly overhead. They become disoriented with death. There is grief in altitude. How do the angels stand it? Look up; they're gone. *Offer food (but very little): tea, coffee, bouillon, a little thin toast, a poached egg.* Empty sky above the black locust.

Altered States

Once I adored a psychic, a long-legged one. Psychic means, *I see you.*

Night was her familiar parlor. "I have a problem," she told me,
"I dream other people's dreams." Her pale eyelashes fluttered.
"I see a trip over water, a mysterious, dark-haired man, a paddle-ball
tournament, and an incident with Baked Alaska." I liked her.
But when I cracked her wide open, she was dark inside.

"Have you ever heard of ghost lovers?" she asked.

People who love ghosts? I wondered between kisses.

"Ghosts who love people. Beautiful women who seduce
for a single night. When they leave, centuries have passed."

"I've heard that story," I said, "only it wasn't beautiful women;
it was dwarves. And it wasn't centuries, but it was a very long time.
And he wasn't seduced, he fell asleep. Except for that, it's the same story."

"The newly dead are allowed to control the weather," she went on.
"It's consolation for never again feeling it on their faces."

"That explains why it's raining cats and dogs," I said.
Garden of Earthly Faucets.

"The living carry us inside them like pearls," she whispered in my ear.
"To close your eyes is to travel. We all keep one another
under surveillance."   She began to snow.

ERIKA MEITNER

In/Exhaustible

Martinsville, Virginia

The billboards into town advertise SOUTHERN GUN
& PAWN, SLOT CARS, say EVERYONE'S PREAPPROVED!
BEST DEAL ON A HOME, PERIOD—the prefabs that come

in halves on the back of trucks labeled WIDE LOAD,
and this was a manufacturing town, until the factories
closed up shop, the warehouses turned to churches

with food pantries, roadways littered with signs:
ARE YOUR BILLS CRIPPLING YOU? PSALM 75:1. FERGUSON
TIRE: WE BUY GOLD, then WELCOME TO MARTINSVILLE—

A CITY WITHOUT LIMITS says the sign on the road in,
and there behind the rows of shotgun houses, a dye plant,
abandoned, two mottled smokestacks rising like goalposts,

no longer pumping out anything of worth near the sign
that says BANKRUPTCY COULD BE YOUR SOLUTION (ALL WELCOME),
the sign that says WE LOVE YOU PASTOR. GET WELL SOON.

The sign says CASH FOR OLD BROKEN JEWELRY, and this
is a town where everyone's broke or gone. It is
Christmastime in Martinsville, and Santa in his red robes,

in his Shriner's hat, stands regal and fat in the darkened
consignment store. Molded sheep rest on cotton batting
near a nest made from hay. The faded wise men kneel

with hands clasped, gazing at that baby with outstretched arms.
In another window, lit-up swaying snowmen sharing a hymnal,
and the plastic baby rests among doves, nestled by a lady

in blue robes with her head bowed. This is a city
of supplication, of duct-taped and empty storefronts,
of faded holiday ornaments, where downtown businesses

only open three days a week—a city that left its smokestacks
raised in prayer to the signs, and the sign says HIGHEST PRICES
PAID IN CASH, says HUGE FURNITURE & MATTRESS SALE.

Some billboards quote a politician: ATTRACTING NEW JOBS
but the local radio talk show has callers buzzing, all asking
the same question: "When is our train gonna come in when

is our train comin' in where is that train," and can you hear it
in the peeling storefronts, the empty storage facilities,
the degree-completion joints? The walk-ins welcome,

the spider-webbed glass, the abandoned call centers?
People speak of your wonderful deeds. The plastic families
wear wire halos, and fold their arms to wait and wait.

Someone will bring work. The smokestacks
are out of breath. The sign at Lays It Away
says HAPPY THANKSGIVING TO ALL AND GOD BLESS.

The Language of Happiness

is not present if there has been a change of partners
(there has been no change of partners)

is the house with a notice taped to the door
& abandoned glow-in-the-dark stars still adhered
to the foreclosed ceiling & the developer

says it will never sell—the basement has been
condemned, did you see the exposed rebar?

The language of happiness
is an inherently inwardly focused experience
is a private affair
is the new black

because my mother went
to the shrouded grave of the Rebbe
& Jesus loves my body like

an empty plastic egg that breaks
in half at the waist waiting to be filled
with small gifts (if we were lying

we'd clap our mouths) I'm just
not telling you everything
youbetterbelieve & blessyourheart

is always stressful,
this language of happiness
is wrecking our friendship
(you're pregnant)

is hectic: I drive the highway
& drive the highway & drive
the highway—you get the picture—
& wait for a woman to say my name
in the waiting room of the language

of happiness we are engaged in collusion
to solve a common problem that is often
quickly treatable, a condition of the [inexplicable]
that impairs conception

the language of happiness is not bracketed—
three unprotected years of nature & then some
for a common problem, a system, an inability
despite an act of love strongly associated
with a body, dear body, can you be

a speeding cab that stops to pick up
a passenger, even if you're off duty?
The driver is on his cell phone again.

We're on the West Side Highway, body,
& behind those lit windows people
are folding & folding & folding
themselves in half like paper.
O fortune-teller. O future.

Correspondence

I drive around in my small, old Honda Civic
and play music that reminds me of driving
the same car when it was new but no larger.

The Civic held four people, but now, with the car seat
and its five-point safety harness, it holds three.
There are Goldfish crackers ground into the floor mats.

My husband is the bassist in a local bar band.
They play classic-rock covers, and though my husband
hates classic rock, he loves his powder-blue bass.

He loves playing in a band. He loves when Frank,
the owner of the bar, gets drunk and tells the band
how much he loves them. They have a monthly gig.

He makes fifty dollars a night when he plays 622.
There are things that are broken beyond repair,
but my marriage isn't one of them.

I am not telling you any of this.
Everything I am telling you is in that letter.
I will not tell you about the fact that I thought

praying mantises were an endangered species
when I was a kid. That was in the seventies.
If I think too much about my childhood,

I will feel too old to write you a letter.
The Internet tells me that this is a long-standing
urban legend; killing a praying mantis was never

illegal or subject to a fine. The origin of the myth
is unknown. Mantises are beneficial to gardens they live in.
Here it seems to make sense to evoke Eden,

but I won't. My son loves praying mantises.
He goes outside each night after dinner to *look for guys*,
and finds them tucked into the spiky barberry bushes.

I will not write you about my son, and if I mention
Eden, it would be to tell you that there's no such thing.
That you are not the talking snake and I am not

the woman without clothes who offers and offers.
The apple has no knowledge to give us. Our cosmogony
is unclear. This is not a love note, or a prayer,

or a field equation. I hold my cards close to the vest.
You send me a picture of a tattoo you'd like to get
of a compass, and the road unravels in front of my Civic

like a spool of thread. We are a gravitational singularity,
a theory that implicates epistemology, but I am not
rigorous enough in my approach to uncover anything.

You write me a letter.
I write you a letter back.
We go on like this for some time.

We're Here

I T WAS THE NIGHT before the origami convention. Graham's wife, Audra, said that they could still change their minds and get their deposit back. He was pretty sure they couldn't get their deposit back, but he knew if he pointed that out, she would say she didn't care. She said whether they went all depended on how much they loved their son.

"That's easy, then," Graham said. "Because we love Matthew more than anything in the world." They were in the kitchen, speaking softly so Matthew wouldn't hear.

"Exactly!" Audra said. "And I *still* don't know if I can bear to go to a whole weekend of origami lectures in Connecticut."

It was kind of startling, Graham thought, how true that was.

"Well," he said slowly, "there are two of us, so one of us can go to the classes with Matthew and the other one can relax. We'll take turns. Maybe it won't be so bad."

"There's a *dinner dance*," Audra said, in the tone of voice someone might use to say a dog had mange.

"Dear God," Graham said.

"I know!" she said. "I think maybe it's some sort of divine punishment for how superior I felt last summer when the Bergmans had to take their little girls to that American Girl Doll museum in Chicago."

"The Bergmans survived," Graham said. "And so will we."

"I guess," Audra said gloomily. "Maybe we'll meet Matthew's future wife there. Some nice Japanese girl who likes origami and who doesn't mind that Matthew is quiet and wears sweat pants all the time and has an extensive Pokémon collection."

It was awful to hear Matthew summed up that way, and yet Graham knew exactly what she meant.

An hour later, Graham found the phone number.

He was in his study, feeling unsettled. They hardly ever went away for just one night. They went to their beach house for a month during the summer and then a week skiing in March and usually took a week at Christmas to see Audra's family. Graham hated coming home from the Christmas trip, hated how unlived-in the apartment felt, hated the stale smell, the air pockets in the pipes making the faucets spit, the lack of food in the refrigerator, the sense that night was coming on and he didn't have enough provisions, hated how chilly it was until the furnace woke up and drove the cold air out again.

He realized he was out of stamps and went out to ask Audra if she had any.

Audra and Matthew were in Matthew's room and she was saying, "Now, I'm going to put out everything you need to take on your bed, but I'm expecting you to pack it all in your suitcase," and Graham experienced the wave of weariness he sometimes felt when he considered all the steps it would take to make Matthew—any child, but especially Matthew—a functioning adult.

Audra's handbag was on the hall table and Graham opened it and took out her wallet. He knew she sometimes kept an extra stamp or two behind her driver's license, where they wouldn't be lost amid the shuffle of bills and receipts and business cards in the main part of her wallet. But Graham didn't find any stamps. Just a small scrap of yellow paper with the name Jasper written on it and a phone number.

Graham looked at it for a long moment. The handwriting wasn't Audra's.

Audra knew hundreds of people. She had her six best friends, and then her other friends and her mom friends (as she called them) and her work friends and her professional contacts and her army of acquaintances and the man at the bodega and the girl at the library and the woman who ran the bake sale and the boy who found Audra's sweater at the library once and ended up coming to Thanksgiving dinner. (Graham could never quite figure that out.) She knew all those people and probably all of their phone numbers, too, and maybe even one or two of them were named Jasper, but Graham didn't think this particular Jasper fell into any of those categories. Otherwise his phone number would be in Audra's phone or her Rolodex and not folded up and hidden here.

He heard Audra's footsteps and knew she was about to enter the hallway where he stood, but he made no move to put the paper back. Oh, he was not the secretive one here. Let her see him with that yellow scrap of paper, let her say, *Oh, Jasper? He's a commercial artist I work with over on Broadway and I have his number tucked in there because—*

But Audra crossed the hall from Matthew's room to their bedroom without noticing him.

Graham slipped the yellow piece of paper into his pocket and returned Audra's wallet to her handbag. He went into the kitchen and poured himself a glass of wine. He looked out the window for a long moment. Then he started chopping onions to make chili for dinner.

He didn't feel any need to reach into his pocket and make sure the number was still there. He could feel it, bright, like an ember, or a luminescent watch face, or an isotope of radium that would glow for hundreds of years.

They were up early the next morning. Matthew didn't have to be called to the table for once—he showed up before breakfast was even ready, dressed and chattering about the origami classes he wanted to take. As she put Matthew's plate of pancakes in front of him, Audra said, "I can't help but feel that across town, Clayton's wife is doing exactly what I'm doing: making breakfast and listening to an excited male talk about outside reverse folds."

Clayton was Matthew's origami teacher, and they had agreed to give him a ride to the convention. He did indeed seem excited; he was waiting outside his apartment building with his backpack already on when they drove up. That and the fact that Clayton's wife was with him made him seem very juvenile to Graham, as though they were picking up a friend of Matthew's rather than a grown man.

Clayton and his wife resembled each other: tall, lean, gray-haired, bespectacled. The only real difference seemed to be that Clayton wore an outfit so mundane it defied description and his wife wore a cherry-red warm-up suit and matching red earrings made of extremely small paper airplanes.

"Hello, Pearl," Audra said as they got out of the car, and Graham was grateful because he couldn't have remembered Clayton's wife's name if he'd been left in a prison cell for five years with nothing else to do.

"Hello, Audra," Pearl said cheerfully. "Hi Graham, and hi Matthew!" She had to lean down to say the last through the car window because Matthew hadn't gotten out.

"Let's get going, shall we?" Clayton said.

"Good-bye, dear," Pearl said.

Clayton was already getting in the backseat with Matthew. "Bye!" he called.

Audra and Graham said their farewells, too, and Pearl smiled and waved. She turned to walk back into the apartment building, off to enjoy a presumably origami-free weekend. Graham felt a pang of envy so sharp it was like a physical blow.

The feeling that Clayton was ten instead of in his fifties remained. He took forever to buckle his seat belt, and he adjusted his air-conditioning vent far more than could have actually been necessary. He opened and shut the cup holder quite a few times, and probably would have put the windows up and down, too, except that Graham had locked them as soon as he'd noticed Clayton's preoccupation with the cup holder.

Audra must have felt it, too, because after a few minutes, she said, "Clayton, can I ask you not to bang the armrest up and down?" exactly the way she would have said it to Matthew.

Clayton stopped his fidgeting but still didn't sit back in his seat. "This is my favorite weekend of the whole year," he said—which was so depressing that Graham thought he might involuntarily plunge the car into the East River.

As Graham wove through the lower Manhattan traffic, Clayton and Matthew talked about origami, about double rabbit ears, crimps, double sinks, closed sinks, and their shared disdain for people who could not fold a bird base from memory. (Graham gathered this last was necessary to qualify for the more advanced classes.) Then they moved on to discussing *Star Wars*, which Matthew loved, and apparently Clayton also loved, although he pretended to be interested in it only in an academic, linguistic sort of way, talking about whether Old Galactic Standard was based on a mix of Durese and Bothese, or whether it was influenced by Dromnyr, which they speak on Vulta.

Audra said something but Graham was so busy wondering how he and Audra could have been such *idiots* as to leave their beloved child in the care of someone so clearly insane that he didn't hear what it was.

"What?" he asked.

"I said that it made me feel old, the way they're talking about Anakin Skywalker, and I can only remember Luke Skywalker," Audra said.

"Oh, well, now, Anakin—" Clayton began from the back.

"It's OK," Audra said hastily. "I don't need to know."

The traffic and the conversation were making Graham's head ache, but then suddenly they were out of the city and on I-95 and the day was beautiful and the leaves around them were almost gaudy with fall color, the red ones as bright as candy apples. The hum of tires on the highway seemed to make both Matthew and Clayton sleepy and their conversation dwindled to sporadic half sentences like, "But if Cloud City is on Bespin . . ."

Audra put in a Leo Kottke CD, nice and soft and gentle. If it weren't for the piece of paper with the phone number on it in his pocket, Graham would have been almost happy.

As soon as they got to the hotel, Matthew and Clayton went off to look at the model menus set up in the conference rooms, and Graham and Audra waited in line in the lobby to check in. Audra was carrying her overnight bag with both hands and leaned back slightly to balance the weight, bouncing it against her knees.

"What I don't understand about origami," she said to Graham in her normal speaking voice, "is why can't anyone like it a *little* bit? Why aren't there nice, well-rounded people who enjoy a bit of origami, the way there are nice, well-rounded people who enjoy a bit of bondage?"

It seemed to Graham that a silence spread out from them, like ripples from a pebble thrown into a pond. But with this crowd, it was hard to imagine whether they were more offended by her first sentence or her second.

Audra continued, oblivious. "I mean, it's like miniature trains or dog shows. It takes over people's lives and they end up going to conventions. It's not like, you know, gardening or sailing or something you just have as a hobby."

Like bondage, Graham was sure the rest of the lobby mentally added.

A portly Asian man in line in front of them turned around. "I take it you don't fold," he said stiffly to Audra.

She gave him her friendliest smile. "No, I don't."

"Then why are you here?" he asked.

"We're here because we love our son," Audra said in a bold, sincere, preachy tone Graham had never heard her use before. Then she looked thoughtful and added in her usual voice, "Plus, we didn't want to be outdone by the Bergmans."

"And your son," the Asian man continued, "—is he passionate about origami?"

"It's pretty much a way of life for him," Audra said. "But we're hoping he'll outgrow it." She stuck out her hand. "I'm Audra Daltry."

The man shook her hand. "I am Li."

"The Amazing Li!" Audra exclaimed. "You teach the class where they fold the praying mantis! Matthew can't wait."

It was amazing, Graham thought, that even origami geeks were susceptible to pretty women flattering them. It was kind of comforting, actually. It gave him hope for Matthew.

There were only five people in line ahead of the Amazing Li but by the time Li reached the front desk, Audra had found out that he had once broken both wrists in a tree-climbing accident and thought he'd go crazy not doing origami for six weeks, and that he was having trouble finding a girl his parents would approve of because they were so old-fashioned and, well, Chinese, and that he really disliked the taste of canned soups, chicken noodle in particular.

Graham had often wondered how Audra got people to tell her everything about themselves so quickly. Once he had asked her and she'd said vaguely, "Oh, I don't know, I guess I think life is too short for all that crap about 'Where are you from?' and 'Do you play the zither?'"

The zither! On what planet was "Do you play the zither?" considered normal small talk? But no matter. What mattered was who Jasper was, or how Audra had met him, and all the things she no doubt knew about *him*.

Graham took Matthew to his first class: The F-16 Fighting Falcon. The man teaching the class called himself Captain Jim, and he fit the part: tall, imposing, silver crew cut, solid jaw, commanding voice. But Graham wondered whether he was actually a retired Air Force captain who had figured out how to fold an incredibly complicated design, or a crazy origami person who figured out the design and then adopted the military persona. Graham sighed. There were so many crazy people in origami.

Matthew had only been allowed to attend the more advanced classes if accompanied by an adult, but Graham knew that Matthew wouldn't need any help. They sat at a table together and Graham read the *Wall Street Journal* and drank a cup of coffee and wondered what Audra was doing—had she noticed Jasper's number was missing from her wallet? Even if she had never called him, did she sometimes take that scrap of paper out and smooth it against the leg of her jeans? And then Captain Jim was standing at their table and admiring Matthew's work.

"Well, look at this," Captain Jim said in his authoritative voice, startling Graham. He picked up Matthew's partially folded airplane and flexed it slightly, checking the folds. Then he looked sharply at Matthew. "How old are you?"

"Ten," Matthew said. "Can I have my paper back?"

Captain Jim gave it to him. "It's interesting," he said. "You are two folds ahead of my instructions. How did you know what I was going to say?"

"I just knew," Matthew said.

Captain Jim nodded. He didn't seem to find Matthew's answer odd, or care that Matthew didn't want to discuss it. He looked at Graham and said, "He has very unusual ability."

Graham smiled but said nothing. He thought, as he sometimes did, that Matthew's origami ability was like a rampart they'd erected to shield them from the rest of the world, and Graham and Audra crouched behind it. People looked and saw only the handsome little boy with the unusual talent. They did not know of the struggles to teach Matthew to tie his shoes, or ride a bike, or try new foods, or wear clothes with scratchy tags, or have his toenails clipped, or understand sarcasm. They did not know that sometimes Graham would be willing to exchange all that origami talent for just a little sarcasm.

After class, they met Audra in the hotel coffee shop for lunch. Matthew was so dazed and dreamy that Graham had to keep reminding him to take bites. He practically had to remind him to chew and swallow.

When Audra asked Matthew how class was, he said, "Great!" and his face glowed with happiness but he didn't elaborate. Audra glanced at Graham, looking amused, but she didn't press. They knew how to handle Matthew by now, and when he was this overwhelmed by something, even overwhelmed in a good way, they let him be.

Instead Audra told Graham that while he'd been in class (she made it sound like he was the one who wanted to go), she had unpacked their suitcases, removed the macadamia nuts from the minibar so Matthew wouldn't eat them, called down to the front desk for extra conditioner, explored the fitness room, done some yoga, and bought a knockoff of a Chloé handbag in the parking lot from a Hispanic man named Sugar.

She had the handbag with her, in an ordinary plastic grocery bag, and she took it out and showed it to Graham. It was a deep mahogany color, with about a hundred zippered compartments, and looked large enough to hold a poodle comfortably.

"How much did you pay for that?" he asked.

She beamed. "Fifty dollars!"

"That's amazing," he said. "I think you've done really well."

He didn't actually think that. He actually thought there was a limit on how many handbags any one person needed and that limit was probably one. But Graham thought that the secret to understanding women (if in fact there was a secret and they could be understood at all) was to admire their purchases. Approve of the stuff they brought home after shopping and they thought you were wonderful.

Audra looked at him happily and put the handbag on the table and began showing him all the little compartments and telling him what she planned to keep in each one.

"Now Sugar told me that the lining is actually the same as the lining in a real Chloé bag," she said. "Apparently the factories in China always make extra and sell it and the companies know but they just consider it part of the cost of doing business. So the only real difference is the quality of leather, and—"

There was more like this, but Graham didn't listen to it, although he kept an attentive look on his face. Audra hated it when he did this, but he still couldn't stop himself. She didn't understand that it wasn't that he wanted her to be quiet; it was that he didn't want to be held accountable for paying attention. He liked the sound of her voice, which was warm and bubbly, and it flowed over Graham, as cozy as bathwater, as comforting as tea.

The name Jasper and the fact that the number was written on a fragment of legal-pad paper made Graham picture a lawyer, someone older and respectable and dependable. Someone like Graham himself. And wouldn't that make sense? Didn't most criminals get caught because they made the same mistakes over and over, because they couldn't break familiar patterns?

So when Audra took Matthew to his afternoon class and Graham went into the bathroom and changed the settings on his cell phone to disable his caller ID and dialed the number written below Jasper's name, he was expecting a mellow, confident voice to answer. Instead it went straight to voice mail and a man said, "Hey, this is Jasper. Leave a message."

There was a hurried quality to the voice that Graham associated with young people: breathless, staccato, busy.

He rapidly abandoned the mental image of the older man with the short white hair and the blue eyes and the long, interesting face (who, Graham realized suddenly, was the lawyer who'd drawn up his will) and replaced it with the image of a tall, thin young man with unruly dark hair and horn-rimmed glasses. Then he realized he was thinking of a children's folk singer he'd taken Matthew to see last month. Apparently he was so lacking in imagination that he couldn't visualize someone he'd never met.

Hey, this is Jasper. Leave a message. Hardly words to haunt you.

He knew he should throw the piece of paper with the phone number away, or better yet, flush it down the toilet. Graham had a poor memory for phone numbers and he wouldn't be able to recall this one (even this one) a week from now. That would be the sensible thing to do. Get rid of the number, clear it from his phone, forget about it, let Audra think it had fallen out of her wallet.

But instead Graham put the number back in his pocket and splashed cold water on his face, already thinking about when he might call again, and what he might say. Criminals were not the only people who made the same mistakes over and over again.

Graham put on a suit for dinner and then sat on one of the beds in the hotel room and waited for Audra to get ready. They were late but he didn't try to rush her. By now he was used to being late wherever they went. She was wearing a butterscotch-colored velvet dress, with a tight bodice and long skirt. She had owned it for many years—in fact, it had been her backup choice for a wedding dress. But she'd stuck with her first choice and married Graham wearing jeans and an ivory blouse of shattered silk. Graham could still remember the feel of that blouse, its silky-rough texture against his fingers when he put his hand on the small of Audra's back.

He watched Audra as she pinned her hair up. It always surprised him that a woman whose hair was not even long enough to touch her shoulders could have so many hairstyles. She clipped on dangly earrings and then turned to face him.

"You look beautiful," he said sincerely. "I'm sure you'll be the most beautiful woman there tonight."

She laughed. "I'm not sure that's all that much of a compliment, given this group," she said. "But thank you."

They retrieved Matthew from the lobby, where he was examining a display of origami animals, and went into dinner and found the table with their name cards. Graham was sitting between Audra and Matthew and next to Matthew was Clayton, and next to Audra was Li. ("Li!" Audra exclaimed, the way someone might cry "Grandma!" at Thanksgiving.) On Clayton's other side was a girl of about thirty, who Graham thought would be really pretty if she weren't so full of hard edges. Her flat blond hair hung past her shoulders and was cut straight across with what appeared to be razor precision. She had a nice but very square jaw, and her eyebrows were straight lines without a hint of arch. She wore wire-rimmed glasses and the lenses were perfect rectangles. Her dress was stiff and white, with a row of gold buttons marching down the front.

Her name was just as hard-edged. "Trina," she said when Graham introduced himself and Matthew. "And you must be the Matthew everyone's talking about."

Matthew looked puzzled. "Why is everyone talking about me?"

"Because you're so good at origami," Trina said.

"But everyone here is good at origami," Matthew said. "Well, except one lady who couldn't collapse multiple creases."

Graham expected the service to be awful, but to his surprise the waitstaff were efficient and he was pleased that instead of taking individual drink orders, they put entire bottles of wine on the tables. As Graham filled up his glass and Audra's, Li and Trina and Clayton pulled stacks of origami paper from their bags (Clayton had his backpack and Li had a man purse of some sort) and began folding. Audra laughed and reached into her own handbag and produced a stack for Matthew. "I don't leave home without it."

With four of them folding, conversation was somewhat stilted, although conversation was never that stilted with Audra around. Soon she had them telling her about last year's convention and how someone named Joe got locked in the men's room and missed all of lunch and part of the advanced snowflake workshop.

Graham reached for the bottle of red wine nearest him and found that Audra's hand was already on it. They traded looks. *Let's get drunk*, his look said. *How else can we get through this?* hers said. Audra took her hand from the bottle and held out her glass, and he recognized a tiny flourish in the gesture, a sign of Audra making the decision to let herself go. He knew her most minute gesture, her most subtle turn of mind. There was no way she kept a secret—a meaningful secret—from him.

Graham went to the bathroom between the first and second course and took a circuitous route back to the table, hoping it would take a long time and spare him having to make conversation with Clayton and Trina and Li. And so it was that he was walking aimlessly past a set of French doors leading to a balcony on the other side of the hotel and he looked out and saw Audra.

She was talking on her cell phone and pacing back and forth in the cold October air, her long velvet dress whirling prettily around her ankles every time she turned. The balcony was in darkness, except for the squares of light that fell from the windows of the hotel along one side, and it was through these patches of brightness that Audra moved. Her auburn hair appeared much darker and her skin much paler than usual, and her butterscotch-colored gown was a hundred shades of gold where the folds of it caught the light. Oh, Audra was wrong when she complained that Graham was not a visual person, that he had no memory for specific hues, that he could not recognize the simplest pigments, that he grew impatient when she got out her color boards. (Actually, she was right about the color boards.) For here was Graham, drinking in the very sight of her, and wishing he were a painter or photographer so he could capture the way she looked forever. Here he was thinking that her eyes were like pools of still water when she looked up at him and that the lock of wavy hair the wind blew across her face was like a dark tendril of ivy on a marble statue.

She saw him and gave a slight wave. Then she said something into the phone and took it from her ear, turned it off, and slid it into her handbag.

Graham opened the French doors and she came inside, along with a gust of cold air.

"I was talking to Lorelei," she said, slipping her arm through his. "I wanted to tell her about my new handbag."

It didn't strike Graham as at all unusual or unbelievable that Audra would call her friend Lorelei to talk about her new handbag (Audra had called Lorelei from their *honeymoon* to describe a coconut-curry sauce), but suddenly he wondered if it was unusual for Audra to tell him who she had been talking to. Did she normally do that? Or was she trying to prevent him from asking, from wondering? Graham tried to remember, and since Audra talked on the phone constantly, he should have millions of incidents to compare with this one, millions of incidents to use to calibrate her behavior. And yet he couldn't remember a single time.

He put his hand over hers on his arm. Her fingers were cold and he wondered suddenly how long she'd been out there.

He could only be certain of one thing. He couldn't go on like this.

The wine was working. Dinner no longer seemed to Graham like an extended running track with a long series of conversational hurdles he had to force himself over. In fact, he didn't have to talk at all. Matthew was quiet beside him, happy with the endless French fries and milk shakes that the waiters brought, and his stack of origami paper.

Clayton and Trina were deep in discussion about something, Graham couldn't hear what, exactly. But Clayton was even more hyper and worked up than usual and Trina nodded when he spoke in a manner that reminded Graham of the way North Korean delegates nodded when the Dear Leader gave political speeches. Occasionally she put her hand on Clayton's arm and leaned closer.

On his other side, Li was teaching Audra how to fold a square of paper into sixty-fourths. Graham felt impatient despite the wine. Audra didn't care about how to fold a paper into sixty-fourths any more than he did. Why couldn't she talk to him, when he was sitting right here?

Audra was saying whenever she tried this with Matthew, she ended up with a rectangle, not a square, and Li said that could happen with machine-made paper if you weren't careful, and Audra said why was that, and Li said it was because in machine-made papers, the fibers are aligned, and Audra said that was so interesting, and Li said modestly that he didn't see any problem with having slightly off-square paper for tessellations, and Audra said he must be the most amazing teacher, and Li said, "I am so fucking turned on, you wouldn't believe it."

(Actually, Li didn't say that last part, but Graham was pretty sure it was true. Who wouldn't be turned on having Audra hang on your every word while you talked about your favorite subject and got to look down the front of the velvet dress, which was very low-cut?)

Finally the others left to go to the dessert buffet and Audra moved her chair so she was nestled up to Graham. "What do you think of Trina?" she asked in a low voice.

"I think she'd be pretty if she were a little . . . softer," Graham said.

"Oh, I didn't mean her looks," Audra said, "because, please, those shoulder pads! Is there a Van Halen concert I didn't know about?"

She said things like that occasionally, which Graham found absolutely inscrutable. She might as well have been speaking whatever they speak on Vulta.

"What I *meant*," Audra continued, "is, do you think she's flirting with Clayton?"

Graham looked over at Trina and Clayton, who were going through the dessert line together. Trina kept picking up desserts with the serving tongs and inspecting them, and then putting them back. Clayton appeared to be making helpful suggestions.

"That did occur to me, yes," he said finally.

"Look, I know he's making an origami candy cane out of fifty triangular units," Audra said. "And that must be very exciting to her. But honestly, can't she see that he's just a super-skinny guy in weird jeans?"

There was no one in all the world he'd rather sit next to.

*   *   *

Audra was so sleepy and tipsy from all the wine that she wanted to go straight to bed after dinner. Graham had a far greater tolerance for alcohol. The wine had only relaxed him. So he sent her on ahead to the room and he took Matthew up to the All-Night Folding Room, which was set up in one of the conference rooms.

Graham thought that the main problem with the All-Night Folding Room was that there was no one around to make fun of the All-Night Folding Room with. Everyone there seemed to take it very seriously. They were gathered in small clusters around different models, folding intently. A few instructors wandered from group to group, but there was little conversation and no background music, just the rustle and snap of many papers being folded.

Matthew left Graham's side and went to one of the tables, and the people there greeted him and quickly made space for him. Their manner was so much more welcoming and accepting than the kids' on the playground at Matthew's school that Graham's heart squeezed briefly with pain.

He waited until Matthew was settled and then he stepped out of the ballroom and found a quiet corner. He took out his cell phone and Jasper's number and dialed.

A girl answered, saying, "Jasper's phone."

Graham swallowed. "Could I speak to Jasper, please?"

"Sure," the girl said. "Hang on."

So there was a girl in Jasper's life and he let her answer his phone. Both of those were good signs.

"Hello?" It was Jasper now, the same voice as on the message.

"Hello," Graham said. "You don't know me but my name is Peter and I'm a friend of Audra's and she has a message for you."

"Friend of whose?" Jasper asked. Graham could detect no hesitation. He sounded open and friendly, honestly confused.

"Audra's," Graham said.

"Who's that?

"Audra Daltry? Graphic designer?"

"I'm a photographer," Jasper said. Again, Graham heard that breathless, energetic sound in his voice, as though he were hopping on one foot or putting on his shoes while he talked. "I know dozens of graphic designers."

"Who is it?" the girl asked in the background.

"Someone calling about a designer," Jasper said.

"We have to go," the girl said. Graham wondered where they were going at 10:30 PM. But that was young people for you.

"I know," Jasper said. "You go on out. I'll be there in a sec. Wait, take my blue—no, right, that one, thanks."

Graham smiled slightly at their shorthand. Every couple had that. "I'm sorry," he said, feeling foolish. "I must have the wrong number."

"No problem," Jasper said.

"Sorry to have bothered you," Graham said. "Good-bye." He could feel his whole body relaxing, relief flowing from the hand that held the phone all the way through him.

"Wait," Jasper said. "What was the message?"

Graham gripped the phone harder. "What?"

"You said she had a message for me," Jasper said. "What was it?"

Graham was silent. Most people are uncomfortable with silence and will eventually say something to fill it. He waited to hear what Jasper would say. "Was it—"

But suddenly Graham couldn't bear to hear any more. "It doesn't matter," he said quickly. "Good-bye." He ended the call.

His heart was thudding and he could barely swallow. It had been a mistake to call. The worst decision possible. If there was anything to know, he didn't want to know it. He couldn't bear to know it. His heart would burst under the weight of it. He realized that now.

In the morning, Audra was so hung over that Graham sent Matthew down to Clayton's room to tell him that they would leave an hour later than they'd planned. Audra stayed in bed with the pillow pulled over her head, and Graham sat in a chair and leaned his head carefully against the back of it, taking small sips from a glass of water. He was a little hung over, too.

Matthew was back five minutes later. "Clayton was in the shower but the girl said she'd tell him."

"What girl?" Graham asked. "Are you sure you went to the right room?"

Audra sat up on one elbow.

"Yes, I went to the right room," Matthew said. "Room 471." Matthew never made mistakes when it came to numbers. "And I did like you said, I knocked and the girl answered and I said that Mommy had had too much wine and needed more time."

"I didn't mean for you to say that part—" Graham began and then gave up. He also hadn't specified *not* to say that, and Matthew was so literal.

"What girl, Matthew?" Audra asked. "What did she look like?"

"The girl who sat at our table last night," Matthew said. "With the blond hair and the glasses. Can I go downstairs and look at the models since I'm ready?"

"Sure," Graham said absently. "Just don't leave the hotel."

Matthew left, banging the door behind him, and Graham and Audra stared at each other. Audra was sitting all the way up now and the strap of her pale yellow nightgown slid down one arm. She always wore pale nightgowns, she said, because men liked it when they could see her nipples through the fabric. (She had told him this on their first date, cheerfully, while she ate a cheeseburger.) Graham could see her nipples now, and he liked it. But the thought of Jasper seeing them and liking them made Graham feel as though an unseen person had suddenly laid a cold hand on his chest, directly over his heart.

"I think it is just unforgiveable of Clayton to do that to Pearl," Audra said. "Especially considering how she wears those itty-bitty paper-airplane earrings all the time."

"You think wearing paper-airplane earrings is the worst part of being married to Clayton?" Graham asked.

"Sure," Audra said. "What do you think the worst part is?"

"Well, having to talk to him or have dinner with him or go to bed with him. Just Clayton himself, I guess," Graham said. "The earrings might be the *best* part of being married to him."

"I just hate him now, though," Audra said. "I can never forgive him for this."

And Graham thought that someone else might take Audra's anger at Clayton as proof that she would never have an affair herself, but he knew differently. He knew that adultery was just like any other vice, pride or gluttony or overspending or vanity. It was easy to condemn other people for it, but then you went right out and did it yourself. It was all different when it was you.

As they got in the car, Graham thought that he and Matthew and Clayton looked like three of the seven ages of man. Matthew the healthy little boy and he and Clayton the stooped gray men at the end. He would even put Clayton as the final man, though Graham was probably older by a few years. Clayton's hangover appeared extreme; he looked dull and shrunken, with none of his usual hyper energy.

"No talking," Audra said to Matthew as they drove out of the parking lot. "Everyone has a headache."

"I don't have a headache," Matthew said.

"Well, the grown-ups do," Audra said. "You just sit quietly and think interesting thoughts. You too, Clayton," she added quickly, leading Graham to believe Clayton must have opened his mouth in protest.

In less than fifteen minutes, Matthew and Clayton were asleep. Graham saw them in the rearview mirror and turned to smile at Audra but she was asleep, too, curled sideways in her seat with her feet tucked under her and her face resting against the upholstery. Her eyelashes were dark crescents on her cheeks.

What was the message?

Graham pushed the thought away.

Audra woke up an hour later and stretched. "Can we stop at an Arby's?"

"Sure." Graham knew she believed Arby's to be the perfect hangover cure.

They saw a sign a few exits later and Graham pulled into the parking lot. Audra said she had to go into the bathroom so she would go inside and get their food.

Graham stayed in the car. He looked back at Clayton and Matthew, who were still asleep, and saw that Matthew had moved so his head rested against Clayton's shoulder. Looking at him sleeping there so trustingly filled Graham with a love so strong he had to blink back tears. He had been wrong earlier when he thought he would change any part of Matthew, that he would trade any of Matthew's sweet guilelessness for some sarcastic little kid. Matthew was beautiful, perfect, just as he was. Graham loved Matthew, he loved Audra, at that moment he almost loved Clayton. There, in the Arby's parking lot, he felt almost overwhelmed by love for his family, and a certainty of his course of action. He would forget all about Jasper and who he might be to Audra. He would stop observing her, stop monitoring her, stop snooping and hoping to find proof of anything. He would love her and trust her—he did love and trust her!—and his love would bind them together, like the atoms in hydrogen, the compass needle and the North Pole, like the rings around Saturn—

"You will not believe this, but they were out of Horsey Sauce," Audra said, getting in and slamming her door shut. She had a way of bringing him back down to earth.

Graham unlocked the door to the apartment and held it open. Audra walked in, saying, "Home again, home again," and Matthew said, "Jiggety-jig." It was their routine since Matthew's babyhood, and made Graham think instantly of strollers and sippy cups and Cheerios everywhere.

Matthew ran off to his room to do origami, and Audra went to their room to unpack. She always unpacked right away. Graham took the mail and went into his study and sat at his desk.

He went through the mail, checked his e-mail and the stock market. He could hear Audra moving around in the bedroom and kitchen. She seemed restless, opening and shutting the refrigerator, pulling out a chair (he heard the scrape of it on the floor) and then pushing it back in.

She appeared in the doorway wearing an oversized sweater of dark-green yarn. Her face was pale and her hair was pulled back messily, but her smile was as warm and sweet as always. He had married her for that smile. "I'm going down to see Lorelei for a while," she said. Lorelei lived on the third floor of the building and was the reason Audra had wanted to live here. It was sort of like being married to someone in junior high.

"OK," he said.

"Are you alright?" she asked.

"Sure, just tired."

"It makes me so sad that the best thing I can say about this weekend is that it's over," Audra said. She kissed the top of his head. "See you later."

After she left, Graham went into the kitchen and made himself a cup of tea. He felt the same restlessness he'd sensed in Audra. It was that unpleasant feeling of returning to an empty apartment in the late afternoon at a time of year when night came early. It seemed like there should be more to do—groceries to buy, laundry to start, bills to pay, lists to make. But there wasn't.

Graham left his tea sitting on the kitchen counter and walked down the hall to the front door. Audra's handbag rested on a small table there.

He took the piece of paper with Jasper's number from his pocket and put it carefully back in her wallet, exactly as he found it. He vowed that he would never look to see if it was there, not ever again. Eventually, he would forget about it, he would go back to being the person he was before.

He walked back down the hall, stopping to check the thermostat because the apartment felt cold. But it was set at seventy-two the way it always was, and they hadn't turned the heat down when they left anyway. It was only the fact that they'd been away that made him imagine this coolness in his chest, this feeling that he ought to rub his hands together and start the blood flowing. That was ridiculous. It had only been a little more than twenty-four hours, not nearly long enough for a chill to set in.

LANCE LARSEN

To My Muse

When I ask for step-by-step instructions,
you tell me to eavesdrop on blue
herons, to wash in dust,
to take dictation from urban rain.
When I ask where you live,
you say, *Can floating spores be parsed?*

When I attempt to nap my humble way
toward the sublime, you toss
a talking pig into my dreams.
When I shout, "Huzzah!"
you caution that testosterone
is a dangerous fuel to think with.

When I try to footnote desire, you say,
Who can extract sunlight
from a field woozy with pollen and mating
dragonflies? When I ask how long
till I'm famous, you invite me to scribble
my question on hatchling sea turtles

then release them into the starved Pacific.
When I mutter, "When, when
will you visit?" you have already morphed
into a stab of October light
italicizing a hopscotching six-year-old,
all lope and bounce, singing about tornadoes.

Aphorisms for a Lonely Planet

Gesundheit!—as close as I've come to Nietzsche and Heidegger in months.

*

All ants on Earth outweigh all humans—some truths climb your leg for weeks.

*

Why do I assume stargazer lilies are happier than dandelions?

*

Doves—mourning or morning? Both names sound wrongly right.

*

During delivery, we rename the vagina *birth canal*: to help the men of this world think *exit* rather than *entrance*.

*

Dirt doesn't mind that we step on it, just as stars do not pine for our promises.

*

In every dialect of bee, *drone* is a compliment.

*

Historians: failed philosophers. Philosophers: failed poets. Poets: failed historians. Etc.

*

Men rarely pee on their own toilet seats, women even more rarely.

*

What holds the kite up, the wind or a ball of twine?

*

Foolish reader, still trying to use this poem as a mirror?

*

Fifteen-year-old son to his father: "Aren't we all heroine addicts to some degree?"

*

Often I fill the teapot not to slake my thirst but to be summoned by singing.

Junk

The rusty hills of iceboxes
mattresses' swollen ripped bellies
still grinding engines rusty
razor blades reflecting a discarded
kingdom of gurgling toilets
stinking up our backyard
where rats sought refuge
the gum bumps my knees scraped
under my third grade desk
the spinning red stools' tops
at the Model Diner where I sat
alone each endless school day
among blistered forests of
thumbs shadowed eyes shaky hands
going and coming from Bonds
DuPont's and Bausch Lomb
the icy Genesee Falls I skipped
rocks off playing hooky nowhere
else to hide except maybe Main
Street cracking under the weight
of its own lethargy the static voices
announcing Saturday's Yankee games
all the way from New York City
the Friday night drunks waltzing
outside Ringo's Bar & Grill kids
lining up to peep into Susie's
older sister's second cousin's
bathroom window the pasties
swirling inside Fancy Abe's neon lit
den of iniquity Grandma angry at

the goose-stepping newsreels showing
Europe burning the stampeding buffalo
in Panavision the empty cemetery plots
waiting patiently after Father died
Moses's furious brows staring down
from the peeling Big Shul ceiling
Mother whispering an off-key dementia
lullaby not recognizing my wife or
her grandchild though I looked familiar
the fireworks over Lake Ontario every
Fourth of July promising everything would
be OK the old Polish woman screaming
on the downtown bus even after
everyone got off like she could see
what was coming Grandma talking
in Russian to someone in her sleep
who wanted to burn her house down
the musty tools books and clothes
in the unheated back room the orphan tin
on the kitchen door the tiny never smiling
rabbi who came every other Tuesday
the snow burying all the unhappy houses
the stained-glass attic window where I sat
counting all the hours before I could leave

A Moment

A measurement of time
in which dogs live
without regret
or desire to enhance
their reputation
and personal worth.
An idea designed
to shelter contentment
and regulate fretfulness.
A request for calm
and further reflection.
A pause or hesitation
used as a defense
against a horrid memory
or fear of the corner.
A stall for time
in order to regain
one's reasonableness
and equilibrium.
An allotment
requested by those
who've used up
their other options.
A plea for calm.
A ubiquitous cave
of sanity. An end
without
a beginning. A room
in which bad news
resides. A wall
behind which

nothing more
waits to happen.
A desperate limitation.
A grain of sand.
A last breath.
A vast opportunity.
A plea to begin over again.

BRENDAN GALVIN

Lefty

His eyes cannot believe
what his legs are doing. Off the leash
he is stotting on this winter beach,
springing in place like a lamb, now bucking,
flexing the way years ago I watched
two fawns as they climbed Rose's Hill
ranging against each other in fifteen
minutes of play. Lefty the leftover,
last of his litter, whom I brought home
in trepidation because of that,
though the sheen on his coat
and a brainy light in his eyes
promised that he might learn not to mess
in the wrong places and chew up shoes,
and grow with no hurry into a border collie,
a sheep dog full of agreeable surprises,
who might be like Patches was,
knowing when the blueberries are ripe
and raking an arm of the bush
for a mouthful. I have witnesses to that,
and how if you told Finnbarr it was raining,
he'd return from the door to his denning place
under the coffee table. If his tail swiped
a sheet of paper off that table,
he'd pick it off the floor and bring it to me
with a sorry eye, his mouth as useful as
an opposable thumb. And once when I flicked
his nose with a finger in play, he took my hand
as lightly as a nurse might and looked me
in the eye to say, *Please don't do that again.*

Lefty, Lefticus maximus, Leftospirosis,
McLefcowitz, we have worked our way
around mutual distrust. You were worth
more than one trip up that old cart road
in western Maine, far from the doggy Walmarts
and the shepherd with a BS in Nantucket Studies.
If you will give me a throaty hoot after dinner
like Magnus does, or watch birds out the window
a half hour at a time, we will do the beach early
for sunups and to flush the occasional fox
from the tall grass, and hear the wing-thresh
of a pair of tundra swans even before
we see them. When I do the math it's clear
you may be my last dog: last night
I couldn't recall who wrote *The Bothie of
Tober-na-Vuolich*. Finally it came to me
and I said "Arthur Hugh Clough" out loud,
glad to have dodged another blown fuse.
You looked up from the rug, your eyes
agreeing, *Yes, that's it. That's it.*

Grace

The first time i see her, she is crouched by the entrance of the bathroom on the third floor, equal distance between my office and the lecture hall where I teach. She is sobbing, and her shoulders are shaking, so I stop, crouch down to be closer to her level, pat her on the shoulder, and ask her if she's all right. She nods and mumbles something under her breath. Then she lifts her head, wipes away tears with her hands, and smiles at me, a weak smile. "I'm OK," she says. Her voice is faint and comes out like a croak. There is a pause, and then another croak. I'm not sure what she says that second time around, but the sound makes me think of frogs, small and slimy, of Exodus and the second plague, of the inundation of the Nile, of Pharaoh and his magicians, challenging God by creating more frogs. I think of all this because that's what's on my mind those days. That's what I teach that semester. The Old Testament.

I straighten up and look in the direction of my office. There is a yellow cart in the center of the hallway, and not too far from the cart, a janitor is pushing a tall broom across the floor. A clock hangs from the ceiling on the far end of the hallway. I look at it and then I look back down at her. "It's about five PM," I say, fumbling awkwardly with the pendant of my necklace. "They'll be locking up the building soon."

She nods and lifts herself up from the floor. She is clutching a handbag to her front, grasping it as if it is some kind of life support, and then all of a sudden she starts to bawl so hard that she seems to be gasping for air. I pat her on the shoulder again, and somehow I find myself leading her back to my office, pulling out a seat for her, one of the two seats in the room that are reserved for my students. Except I'm not even sure that she's a student of mine. And in my twenty years at the university, I've never seen any of them bawl like this before.

"I'm sorry," I say to her, because I truly am to see her crying so hard. She leans forward on the chair, still clasping her bag, rocking it and herself back and forth. Slowly her sobbing declines until I can only hear the occasional catch of her breath. She rises from her seat and heads for the door.

"If you ever need someone to talk to—" I say. I don't finish.

At the doorway, she turns to look at me. "Thanks," she says. Her head is covered with thin black braids down past her shoulders, and her skin is a dark olive complexion, unique in its hue. Her lips are swollen and reddish, and there are streaks of tears staining her cheeks. I wonder where exactly she is from. As she walks out the door, I find myself thinking what a shame it is that anybody should be made to cry that much.

A few days go by: Thursday, Friday, and the weekend. I've almost forgotten the crying incident by Monday when I step into the lecture hall for my Old Testament class. The class itself is larger than normal, and a different demographic than other graduate courses I've taught, Chaucer, say, or Milton, or even my Greek mythology class. These students are more zealous than any I've had before. I figure that maybe it's the Bible's effect. Or maybe it's a consequence of age, because from the look of things, most of these students are in their thirties and forties, older than my typical set of students. And, unlike former students, these ones are quite fond of scheduling meetings with me. They do it with such alarming frequency that at certain points in the semester, I consider putting a cap on the number of visits allowed per student. Not because I don't want to meet with them, but because after a while, I get tired of hearing the same questions over and over again, questions like why the books of the Old Testament are organized the way they are, or why it is that in Leviticus God bans cripples from approaching his altar. Often enough, my answer is that it's a good question, and that there are several possibilities, all of which are subject to debate.

In any case, I step into the lecture hall, and a group of my students walks in the door with me, making small talk about God and the weather. I nod and smile at the things they say, and after we enter, I head directly to the front of the room, the way I always do. I jot down some Bible verses on the board, write some notes about apodictic law versus casuistic law, about Hammurabi's Code versus the Ten Commandments, about goodness for goodness' sake versus goodness with an eye to some type of reward or punishment. I wipe the chalk off my hands and turn around to face the class, and I catch a glimpse of her with the long black braids, sitting in the corner at the very back of the room. I smile. She looks down. I figure she's embarrassed about the crying, so I go on with the lecture, and I try not to look her way.

After class, I'm packing up my notes, stuffing my Bible into my bag, when I hear her voice.

"Excuse me," she says. "I'm Grace," she says.

She asks me when my office hours are. I tell her. Thursday mornings, nine AM to twelve noon. She nods. I smile. She doesn't smile back. She says, "I'd like to come in and talk to you about the Bible."

"Sure," I say. No surprise there. That's all they're coming in to talk to me about this semester.

Before she turns around, I am struck by the intensity of her expression. There is something vulnerable about her, something akin to old age. I think how such seriousness should be accompanied by a fine set of wrinkles across the forehead, or around the eyes and mouth. But she is young, maybe a couple of years younger than my own daughter, who is thirty, certainly significantly younger than what I imagine to be the average age for the students in this particular class. Her face is so serious and her eyes so penetrating. But there are no wrinkles to be seen.

She turns to leave, and I notice the way her braids dangle from her shoulders, and something about the way they move as she walks makes me want to reach out and touch them. But I remain where I am and watch her walk out of the class, and I think of her name, Grace, and how there couldn't be a more fitting name for her.

On Thursday, I'm sitting in my office with my door cracked open, flipping through my stack of mail, when she knocks on the door. I invite her in, and she shuts the door behind her. They sometimes do, when what they have to talk to me about is personal.

I take in her face again—that startling combination of youth and old age—and I think how her clothes are an extension of that paradox: a white dress shirt, buttoned almost to the very top, prudishly, though I can see the outline of her bra through the white, diaphanous cotton. She has tucked the bottom of the blouse into the waistline of her grayish tweed skirt. On her feet, she wears simple leather slippers. Her only jewelry is a pair of pearl earrings. A very neat presentation, which makes me aware of my own not-so-tidy look. I tug the hem of my untucked shirt, as if tugging will straighten out the wrinkles. I fuss with my earrings, and I'm grateful that I even remembered them today. I run my fingers through my hair and hope that I catch and put back into place any strays. I cross my legs under the table, and I ask her to take a seat.

She is holding her Bible, a small King James with a maroon cover, and all over the inside are pink and yellow Post-it notes, as if she's been doing some serious research.

She clears her throat, and tells me she has a few questions. That they are probably silly questions, but that she would like to see what I think, since I'm the only Bible scholar she knows with an academic background. I'll probably give her a different take on things than she's used to getting, she says. She speaks with a bit of an accent, barely perceptible, just enough for me to conclude that she's probably from somewhere as unusual as her looks suggest.

She quotes me 2 Timothy: "All scripture is given by inspiration of God, and is profitable for doctrine, for reproof, for correction, for instruction in righteousness." She asks me, how exactly do we know that God has inspired the Bible? Because the Bible has caused quite a bit of destruction in the world, she says. How do we really know that God even approves of some of the things in the Bible?

I smile and tell her, "Sorry, I'm only dealing with the Old Testament this semester. Timothy is the New Testament." I start to laugh, because it's meant to be a joke, but her face is thoughtful and disappointed, so I clear my throat, and I apologize.

I tell her that religion is all about faith. And one's faith is a very personal thing.

She tells me that there are things in the Bible that could not possibly be from God, contradictions, like the whole idea of God being a god of peace, but also a god of war. "Which one is it?" she asks. And what about love your neighbor as yourself, and yet, God forbids the cripples from approaching his altar? What kind of God bans the very creatures he created from coming to him just because of imperfections out of their control?

I tell her that she needs to keep in mind that the Bible was written within a particular cultural context. I tell her there are many ways to read it. I say that I believe it was inspired by God in many ways, but it was still written by humans, with human biases, shaped by the existing cultural norms of the time.

She nods and says, "So if humans are making their own rules, and writing the rules down in the Bible, where exactly does the godly inspiration enter?"

"Well," I say, "God inspired them to set down the rules in the first place. And when you look at all the ancient books in the world, none have lasted as long and have had as much influence as the Bible. That in itself is an attestation to some kind of divine inspiration, I think."

"I suppose," she says. "But then how do we know what rules are God's and what rules are man's? I need to know," she says.

"Are you worried about any particular rule?" I ask.

"Like divorce," she says. "Is it adultery to divorce and remarry, or is it permissible?

And shouldn't it at least depend on the specific circumstance? What about in the case of an abusive husband? Must the woman stay?"

I hesitate a bit. I wonder if she's contemplating divorce, or if she's just picking out an example. Then I think of my own divorce, nearly fifteen years ago now. I remember the loneliness of it all, the disappointment in failing at something as important as marriage. "Marriage is a sacred union," I say, even as I'm recalling my own. "When something happens that makes the union no longer sacred, I believe that is grounds enough for divorce."

"But is the Bible OK with that?" she asks. "Is God OK with that?"

"I don't know," I say. "It's difficult to know."

We stay quiet for a while. Then I look up at her. There is a trail of tears coming down one side of her face. The other side is still winning the battle, resisting the tears.

"I'm sorry my class is upsetting you this much," I say.

"No," she says. "It's not your class." She wipes her tears away. "I'm sorry about all this crying," she says.

"Don't be sorry," I say.

She looks at me, then she looks down at her Bible, flips it open. "Thou shalt not lie with mankind, as with womankind: it is abomination." She pauses. "If a man also lie with mankind, as he lieth with a woman, both of them have committed an abomination: they shall surely be put to death."

I'm intrigued by these verses that she reads. All of a sudden the conversation is taking a different turn. I remain quiet and simply listen to see where it'll go.

"Does this also apply to females?" she asks. "Is it also an abomination for women to lie with women?"

Aha, I think. "It's a tricky issue," I say. "Try not to take it all so literally. There are things in the Bible that should not be taken so literally."

"I don't understand," she says.

"Like the word *abomination*," I say. "It's hard to even know what that meant back then. Meanings change over time. It's hard to know."

She looks down at her Bible. She says, "It's hard to know right from wrong, especially when some things feel natural, and yet there are so many people telling you how wrong they are."

I nod, and I think how honest this conversation is. Usually, I'm listening to questions that don't have to do with anything personal. Just demonstrations of intellect and scholarship. I want to hug her and tell her that one day she'll figure it out for herself. But I'm not so sure of that, and so I don't move. Instead I say, "The greatest commandments, according Jesus, are first, love the Lord your God with all your heart and soul and mind. And second, love your neighbor as yourself."

I smile at her. She smiles back. On her way out she tells me thank you for the talk.

"Anytime," I say.

Two weeks later, I'm sitting in my office, my back to the door, when I think I hear a knock so soft that I have to turn around to check if someone is really there. From the opening, I can see a bit of her face, standing by, waiting for me to answer.

I pull open the door, invite her in. She is holding a white paper bag in one hand and a card and an envelope in another. She tells me she's brought something for me. She sits down, signs the card in front of me, and as she's signing it, she's muttering something about my having to excuse her cursive, because she never really learned how to write in cursive. I ask her why. She looks up at me, all thoughtful, and says, "They didn't teach cursive in Nigeria." She puts her head back down and continues to write.

I say, "Oh, I would have thought maybe it's because of your age. I don't believe they're still teaching it in schools these days. I don't believe they've taught it for at least a couple of decades now. Probably they wouldn't have been teaching it for people your age, even if you were in America."

She looks back up at me and smiles. "I'm not so young," she says, handing me the card.

"Does it say something sweet?" I ask, and immediately, I'm embarrassed by the question.

"Not really," she says. "But what it says should be good enough."

I feel the heat rise in my face. I tell her thank you. She gets up, tells me to have a good day. She leaves the room. I take out the card and see a picture of a wide, expansive sky. Above the clouds, the sun is bright.

Inside the card, she has written the words: "I saw this in the store. It somehow reminded me of you." In the bag, a brooch of a hummingbird.

In class the next week, I keep from looking her way. I'm not sure exactly why. Maybe residual embarrassment or something like it.

Another week passes by, and then she comes back to my office. It's the same routine each time, and it repeats every other week or so. She knocks on my door, peeks in, and asks me how I am. I tell her fine. She says, "Good." And then she wishes me a good rest of the day and leaves.

Thanksgiving comes and goes, and we all start to wrap ourselves up with thick scarves and wool mittens.

The last week before Christmas break she knocks on my door, and I tell her to come in. She is wearing a brown hat, some kind of knit, and half her face is covered by a matching scarf. She enters the room, closes the door behind her, raises her hands to her face, and it's only then that I realize that she's upset—and quite a bit angry.

She unravels the scarf from her face, and I see that she is crying. I stand up and hug her. "Somehow it all works out," I say. I used to tell this to myself during my divorce, and the weeks afterward. Then the weeks turned to months, and months to years. And I found myself chanting it less.

She mumbles something about letters, about her mother. Then she stays silent for a while.

"It'll be all right," I say, my arms still wrapped around her. Suddenly I have this image in my head of John Rosenberg making out in his office with that female student of his. I don't remember who it was that walked in on them; it was several years ago. But I know he lost his tenure that way, created a scandal in the department that lasted quite a while. It occurs to me that if someone were to walk into my office at that very moment, things between Grace and me would appear inappropriate. I've never consoled a student like this before. And with my closest family members half a country away, in Massachusetts, it's been a while since I stood this close to anyone, minus cursory hugs from friends and co-workers. It occurs to me that I should take my hands off her waist, but I don't, and, thinking back now, the reason I don't let go is quite clear. But at that very moment, all I am thinking is that I prefer to leave my hands where they are, that anyway, it couldn't possibly be inappropriate, being that I'm a woman, and she's a woman, and I'm probably older than her mother.

After some time, she sighs, an extended sigh, one of those sighs that seem to tumble out after hours and hours of tedious contemplation. Then she tells me that she was the one who signed for the packet the day the first batch of letters came, nearly a year ago.

"What letters?" I ask.

She starts to laugh, softly, as if she's suddenly in some kind of trance, but then she stops. I release her, motioning to a chair, but she makes no move to take the chair. We are still standing there, with a little more space between us—no longer in an embrace—when she really gets into the story.

She tells me that the forecasts that day called for snow, but that the deliveryman only wore the yellow-and-red polo shirt, with a red collar and a red hem around the sleeves. He wore a hat, she says, which, when he removed it, revealed a head of graying hair. She looks at me. "Salt-and-pepper, like yours," she says. Then, she shakes her head slightly and looks down as if suddenly embarrassed or shy.

The DHL man handed her the yellow package with a smile on his face, she says. Always the same deliveryman, she tells me, with the same truck. She thought she knew what the package was, some silly correspondence for her mother from Nigeria, because silly correspondences were often coming for her mother from Nigeria.

It is as if she now grows weary of standing because she proceeds to take the seat that I had offered. I follow her lead and pull out an opposite-facing chair for myself from which I can continue to look directly at her.

"Did I tell you I have a brother?" she asks suddenly.

"No," I say.

She nods. "Arinze," she says. "Five years older than me. When we were little, he and I used to take turns climbing a stool that my mother kept in the attic. It was our playroom, that attic room. It only had one window, which was so near the ceiling that we had to climb the stool to open it up."

My office reminds her a bit of the attic room, she continues, with its exposed brick walls, with the tiny holes between the bricks. Millipedes and centipedes crawled out of the holes in the spring and the summers. This last part comes out like something between a statement and a question, and I wonder if she's asking me about my office or telling me about her mother's attic.

"But it's been years since either of us used the stool," she says, "years since either of us opened or closed the window. Which explains the scent," she says. "Building up and then settling into every corner, into every item in every corner of the room. The scent of mothballs, and of Mentholatum." She laughs softly again, shaking her head as she does. Then she tells me that she's wrong. That my office is nothing like the attic, because even though there are the brick walls and the tiny holes, the scent is missing. "It's a good thing," she says.

I nod and say, "OK."

"I handed the envelope to Mama," she says. As she speaks I can see their kitchen in my head, her mother sitting on the short stool, her legs wrapped around the circumference of the mortar, pounding yam with the pestle. "All this time in

43

America," she says. "And still, Mama must pound her yam in the mortar, the old-fashioned way."

"How long have you been in America?" I ask.

"Years," she says. "Just over ten years." She came at twelve, she tells me. I do the math and find myself disappointed to realize that she's only twenty-two. Her seriousness, her self-possession: I had thought perhaps twenty-eight or twenty-nine.

She breathes deeply and continues. "I walk into the kitchen and hand the envelope to Mama. Meanwhile Arinze is downstairs; I can hear the hammering and the drilling. He is putting together a shelf for Mama. Always stopping by, helping Mama around the house, fixing or putting together something for her. A perfect son, really," she says. "Which is why Mama put him in charge of managing her stores, coordinating the shipments of the products from Nigeria, that sort of thing."

I nod.

"There was a whole batch of letters in the envelope," she says. "And this time they weren't for Mama," she says. "They were all for me."

"From whom?" I ask.

"Men," she says. "Marriage proposals." Her voice begins to break, and something in my stomach takes a nose dive. I tell myself that the nose dive is because I don't want to watch her cry again.

"Do you know the men?" I ask.

She shakes her head and then leans on my shoulder. I can feel the roughness of her braids rubbing my jaw. Her scent is fleshy but sweet.

"There's one," she says. "Obinna." She lifts her head. "An Igbo man who lives in Lagos, Lekki, in one of those big houses with uniformed gatemen. Owns his own accounting firm." She pauses. "Mama likes that part," she says. "The part about owning his own business. And she likes that he really wants to marry me," she says.

She tells me that his letters are filled with things like, "You're the wife of my dreams, my African queen." She pauses, then she exclaims, "How silly it is for Mama to expect me to marry a man I've only seen in pictures!"

I ask her if *he* has seen *her*, if he has any idea what she looks like, or is he just operating under some kind of divine guidance?

She tells me, yes, that he's seen her picture, too. That her mother took the picture herself, that her mother placed the stool by the empty wall of the dining room and asked her to sit there, arranged her braids so that they framed her face and shoulders just so. After posing her, her mother rubbed some maroon lip gloss on her lips and lent her a pair of gold-and-pearl chandelier earrings. Then she snapped pictures until finally she got the one that she said was just right. This was the only picture of Grace that Obinna had seen, as far as she knew. Somehow, she tells me—and she can't even begin to understand how—it was all he needed to make the decision to marry her.

I'm feeling devastated about her having to marry this Obinna guy, and I wonder if it will be terrible, if she will have to endure an unhappy marriage, or if she will come to love him. It occurs to me how little thought I've given to the whole idea of arranged marriages. Until then, it's been a sort of abstract concept. I tell her that I'm sorry.

"Has a date been set?" I ask.

"I don't know," she says. At the beginning of this semester Obinna made the official request to her mother, in a letter. And, of course, she says, her mother said yes, told her that it was all for the best, that Obinna had her best interest at heart. That any girl her age had no business not being married. Any girl would be a fool to decline a man who wanted her as much as Obinna did. All of this, she tells me, happened the day that I found her by the entrance to the bathroom.

I ask her what's been going on in the months since then.

"Waiting," she says. "And praying that Obinna or Mama would have a change of heart."

I say, "No luck, I take it."

She shakes her head. "No luck," she says. She tells me that this morning she finally got the courage to say something to her mother. That she walked down the hallway in their house, climbed up the stairs into the attic, because her mother was there, sorting piles of paper, business papers, or marriage papers. She said to her mother, "I'm not marrying him." As she speaks I imagine her mother hunched over, slowly straightening up, a pair of glasses hanging on the bridge of her nose. At first her mother doesn't answer. And then she clears her throat, adjusts her glasses. "Stop that nonsense," her mother says.

Her brother Arinze walks into the attic room, holding a box, the one into which she assumes her mother will be sorting the piles of paper.

"Mama, I'm not getting married," she says.

Her mother doesn't answer, so she raises her voice and says, "Did you hear me, Mama?"

"She's not deaf," Arinze says.

"Mama?" Grace says, softer.

Her mother still does not answer.

Then suddenly her mother speaks. "All that studying," she says. "You'll marry your studies? Marry your books?" "You already have one degree," her mother says. "But you want another. You'll marry your degrees?"

She doesn't answer.

"Am I talking to the wall?" her mother asks. "Answer me!" And then she doesn't wait for an answer. She says, "Before you know it, you'll look around and find yourself all alone, just you and your degrees. And then what?"

She tells her mother that it's not for her.

"What's not for you?" her mother asks.

"Marriage," she says.

"Marriage is not for you?" her mother scoffs. "Your papa, God rest his soul, would cringe in his grave if he heard you say such nonsense. What good is having that doctorate that you're going for, if your life is empty, no husband, no children?"

"It's not for me," she tells her mother again. But she doesn't tell her mother the entire truth. It's not the marriage part that's not for her. It's the fact that she doesn't like men in the marrying way. She's never been interested in them like that. She tells me this now, though of course I already knew.

"A woman needs to marry, have children," her mother says. "Life is more satisfying that way."

"She'll marry her books and degrees," Arinze says, chuckling.

"Shut up," she tells her brother, in a whisper.

"You shut up," Arinze says. "And better watch how you talk to me, old maid."

"Be quiet," her mother says to her. "You'll get married. That's final." And her mother turns back to the floor, toward the piles of papers that she is sorting.

Grace turns around to leave her mother, to leave her brother, to leave the attic room. But something makes her turn back. So she stands facing her mother, but she fixes her eyes on one of the holes on the brick wall. She takes in slow, calculated breaths to steady her voice. Then she says, calmly, in a clear, firm voice, "I won't."

Suddenly her mother is slapping her, screaming at her about defiance. She is trying to push her mother away, and then she feels Arinze towering above her, pounding his fists down on her shoulders. "Don't you dare disrespect Mama like that!" he shouts. "Don't you dare!" More pounding. She struggles to breathe, but every breath is suffocating, saturated with the scent of mothballs, and of undiluted Mentholatum. And then the brick walls in the room start spinning around her, and her shoulders are throbbing, because she is now down on her knees, she tells me, and still Arinze's fists are pounding down on her.

"I can't," she finishes, like a sigh. I can see the tears in her eyes. I sit there and allow her to lean her head against my shoulder.

Before she leaves, I mention to her the counseling services at the university. I ask her if she's ever been there. She shakes her head. I tell her that perhaps there is someone there who can help her more than I can. She shakes her head again. "Try it out," I tell her, trying to sound adamant. "At least think about it," I say. But even as I say it, there is a part of me that is scared that if she finds the counseling staff helpful, she might stop coming to me.

That night, I take a walk around town. Christmas lights hang above every doorway, and the ground is covered with snow. The air is cold and feels as if it is pricking the skin on my cheeks. I imagine pins and needles, thin, rusting metal wires, stabbing my skin. I tell myself that perhaps this is my punishment, for these new thoughts, these inappropriate desires. Perhaps a little stabbing is what I deserve. All the same, I tug at my scarf and my hat, adjusting them so that they cover the exposed portions of my face.

There is a strong hazelnut aroma in the air. It leads me to a coffee shop, Brewed Awakenings. Even with the cold, the scent is so strong and oddly appeasing, like a balm, that for a moment I consider stopping to buy myself a cup of coffee, even if coffee is not my thing, has never been. But I don't. Instead, I take a seat at one of the outside benches a short distance from the tall glass window. And I breathe in the aroma. And I watch the people inside.

There is a couple sitting by the window. I can't see them clearly at first, because they are seated sideways in the shop, and they are wearing hats, and they have muffled themselves with oversized scarves that appear more like cloaks. Then he removes his hat and scarf, and she does the same. He smiles at her, reaches out and stirs the contents of her cup while she is still struggling to take off her gloves. Their hands come together, his dark skin on her fair skin, and I think of Grace, and I imagine Obinna putting his hand on her. And then the woman takes her cup, takes a sip out of it, and she laughs at something he says. She looks happy, and I find myself wishing that Obinna makes Grace happy like that. So long as she is happy, I say to myself. And I find myself trying really hard to remember if I've ever heard of or read about or watched any stories in which an arranged marriage ends up being successful. Of course the only examples that come to my mind are from the Bible. I think of Isaac, how Abraham asks his servant to go find a wife for him. And that woman ends up being Rebekah. And the servant asks her father for permission to take Rebekah back home to Isaac. And her parents give the permission. She does not know what Isaac looks like; neither does Isaac know what she looks like. And yet the marriage ensues and for all intents and purposes appears to be a success. Of course, the big difference is that Rebekah agrees to marry Isaac.

"Will you go with this man?" they ask her.

"I will go," she says.

Just a few days before Christmas, my daughter calls me from Massachusetts, tells me that because of a mess-up in plans, they will be spending this Christmas with her in-laws, that they will no longer be coming down to be with me. It's been this way since my grandson was born, three Christmases now, and each time she comes up with a new excuse as to why they won't be spending Christmas with me. She tells me it has to be done because her husband's family will be very upset if they don't make it.

"What about me?" I ask.

She says, "Mom, it's just you. He's got the whole family, brothers, sisters, aunts, uncles, cousins. They'll all be angry with me. Please understand," she says. "I'll make it up to you. In the meantime, better for one person to be mad at me than the whole gang."

I tell her fine, that I have research to do and lectures to prepare for anyway. And the truth is that I'd much rather not be dealing with the chaos of family Christmases, all four of us gathered together in the small space of my apartment, the noise and bustle and lack of privacy so different from the order of the lecture hall. Still, it'd be nice to bake pies and help prepare the meal, to sit around and chitchat, catch up. Not to mention that it'd be nice not to have to eat alone, because these days, maybe because of the Christmas season, or the cold weather, I'm feeling more lonely than ever, and eating has begun to feel like a chore, something that needs to be done, a solitary task without any enjoyment in it. In any case, I tell my daughter, "Fine." She thanks me profusely.

I immerse myself in work the entire break, but between the research and the preparation for lectures and conferences, I find myself thinking of Grace. I think of the feeling of her braids on my skin and of her smile and of all that crying she did. I remember her collared dress and her musty perfume scent. And every now and then there is a feeling of dread when I think of the possibility that she will be a married woman the next time I see her.

* * *

The New Year arrives, and then a week later, classes resume. The first week, I don't see Grace. The second week, I'm sure she will show up, but she doesn't. Her name is on the roster for one of my seminars, but she does not appear; nor does she come to office hours. I begin to mope about. Every passing day becomes a great disappointment, though there are those brief moments of hope, moments when I find myself recognizing Grace's features in another young woman. But then the young woman turns around and I see that it's not her, and I'm left feeling even emptier than before.

Then the third week, I'm sitting in my office, flipping through the pages of the New Testament when I hear the knock. She enters without my inviting her in. I'm expecting that she will head straight to one of the two empty seats. Instead she stops near me, hugs me from behind before taking a seat. She apologizes for being gone all this time, for returning so late into the beginning of the semester. She asks me if I had a good Christmas break, and all I can do is nod.

She stretches out her hand to stroke my arm. "I'm sorry," she says. Maybe the look on my face somehow tells her how miserable I've been.

I look down at my arm, at her hand on it. She retracts it, shyly, as if she's suddenly aware of an indiscretion. I want to tell her that I've been thinking of her, but instead I find myself saying, "Are you married now?"

She looks curiously at me, and for a moment I feel as if I am trespassing, as if the question is not mine to ask. But her curious glance quickly fades away, and she shakes her head and tells me no, but that soon she'll be. This time it's I who reaches out and strokes her arm.

"It's OK," she says. "It's not the end of the world."

"Isn't it?" I ask, wanting her to tell me that it is in fact the end of the world, wanting her to begin crying again so that I can hold her.

She shakes her head. "No," she says. Then she clears her throat. "I'd like you to come," she says.

"To your wedding?" I ask.

She nods. It will be in May, after the semester comes to an end, she tells me. It will be held here in America, she says, because it is what Obinna wants. Something to the effect of his taking their marriage as an opportunity to make his first trip to America.

"You'll come?" she says again, this time a question.

I shake my head and tell her I can't. That I'll be teaching the summer session, that it might not even be appropriate for me to attend given that I'm her professor.

"Really?" she asks.

49

"Really," I say, forcing myself to stick to the excuse.

We both stare at each other for some time. Neither of us speaks. Then she says, "I was in Nigeria over the break."

"To see family?" I ask.

She nods.

She tells me her cousin Ogechukwu was getting married, and her mother wanted her to attend the wedding ceremonies, the traditional and the white, to remind her firsthand how authentic Nigerian weddings were done, so that she would know what was expected of her at her own wedding.

She stops there, and when she doesn't continue, I ask whether her brother and her mother went with her.

"Mama went with me," she says. "Not Arinze," she says. Because, she tells me, according to her mother, Arinze already knew the culture, already knew what it meant to be Nigerian. It was she who caused her mother concern.

She tells me her mother is right. That sometimes she barely feels Nigerian, which she knows has never been the case with Arinze. Growing up, Arinze was always speaking Igbo with her mother while she could only understand, not speak, and had to respond in English. Arinze would always swallow his balls of *garri* after dipping them into the soup. She, on the other hand, chewed hers. Arinze knew the Igbo names of all the food items they sold in the store, from the crayfish to the oils to the seeds. He could differentiate *egusi* from *ogbono*. She could not. And, of course, there was the time that Arinze told their mother that he would find himself a good Igbo girl and marry her. He was much younger then, she says, and she laughs a dry, sarcastic laugh. She tells me that perhaps he has changed his mind by now. But even that far back, she says, she had no desire to marry a man, much less a Nigerian man who she'd never actually met.

"Did you finally get to meet him, then?" I ask.

She nods but doesn't say any more. Instead she tells me how an aunt of hers, Aunty Nora, waited for them at the airport gate. How Aunty Nora screamed and danced around and waved her hands in the air when she saw Grace and her mother. The cousin, Ogechukwu, a thin girl with an oval face and prominent cheekbones, accompanied Aunty Nora. Grace tells me that there was something like surrender in Ogechukwu's face. As if hers, too, was an arranged marriage. As if it was also by force.

Anyway, they all hugged and then Ogechukwu and Aunty Nora helped Grace and her mother to carry their luggage out of the airport.

She and her mother only stayed a week, she tells me. They helped to prepare the food for the wedding, pots of *egusi* soup, okra soup, *jellof* rice, fried fish, and of course, the *ishi ewu* delicacy—fried goat head in pepper soup.

They helped to fit Ogechukwu's outfits, too, pinning the sides of the wrappers and the white wedding gown, picking out the beads of her necklaces and the beads of her *jigida*, her waist beads, which were numerous, about fifteen sets altogether, all of different colors. They measured the *jigida*, fitted them, because she would wear them as she danced, and they would jingle, and onto them money would be stuck. But if they were not correctly fitted, the *jigida* would start to descend down Ogechukwu's buttocks, down her thighs, with all the dancing that she would do that day, and all the money would drop with them.

"Sounds very festive," I say, when she finishes. "Very rich in tradition."

She nods. "You should come to mine," she says.

"Will it make you happy?" I ask.

"Happiness is like water," she says. "We're always trying to grab on to it, but it's always slipping between our fingers." She looks down at her hands. "And my fingers are thin."

I'm not sure how to respond, but I say: "I wouldn't know how to behave, all the rites and rituals. I wouldn't know what to wear."

"Dress as you do to teach," she says. "Only remember that after you've dipped your *garri* in your soup, you must swallow, not chew." She laughs. "That will definitely give you away," she says.

"As if that's the only thing," I say.

We both laugh.

February comes and February goes, and March and April, all passing by with the snow and the bitter cold. We resume our meetings, and I find myself looking more and more forward to them, growing more and more impatient for her company.

The weather reports call for sun throughout the week of her wedding. That week we meet as usual in my office, but she asks that we meet again outside of the office, at the park by the river, under the light and dark shadows of the trees. And I agree.

It is midafternoon when I make it to the park. The sun is floating like an orange ball in the sky, reflecting itself on the river. Its rays cause the water to shimmer, like silver and gold threads on a bed of gray silk. I take in the trees which line the trail, spaced several yards apart, and choose a bench near one of these trees. The tree's oblong leaves dangle from frail branches and flutter in the air. I reach out and touch the bark of its trunk, which appears jigsaw-like, akin to craters on the surface of the earth. I am still running my fingers across the surface of the trunk, about to pick at a piece of the bark, when I catch sight of Grace. My heart skips a beat.

She walks toward me holding a small red box, about the size of her small King James. But it is not the same shade of red as her King James, and around the box strands of gold ribbons have been tied into a bow. Others dangle freely in spirals. She approaches, with slow steps and long strides. She is wearing a beige dress that comes down to her ankles. Her shoulders seem to sag, and I feel my own sag in response. Her loose braids sway, and I take them in, thinking how pretty and dark and youthful they are. And suddenly I'm aware of my age, and of my slumping posture, of my gray hair, of the wrinkles around my eyes and mouth. I think how much more my slumping must be aging me. I sit up, square my shoulders, tuck the loose strands of my hair behind my ears, and wait for her to come to me. All the while, I'm wondering what's in the box.

She takes a seat by me on the bench, on a diagonal, so that she is facing me. Her hands rest on her lap. She taps the box softly, then runs her finger along the side of it, along the surface of the ribbons. I watch her fingers move, slowly, delicately. It is almost hypnotic.

I think of Obinna caressing those fingers, and there is resentment in me. I start to imagine her wedding, but it is interrupted by thoughts of my own divorce, of sitting alone by the fireplace at home, listening over and over to the sound of silence, the crackling of wood, the heavy rustling of the leaves outside my windows. And, really, I think, it was all my fault, if it came down to blame. It was my fault for not being able to devote myself to him, to love him completely, the way a wife should her husband. But there'd been something missing for me in the marriage. And I'd been lonely all the while. I'd have been lonelier if I'd stayed. Because, as if in rebellion, certain emotions become amplified at the exact moments when you are expected not to feel them at all.

The river is just ahead, and I turn my eyes to it. I imagine throwing pebbles into it, imagine the small splashes that the pebbles cause as they cut through the surface of the water.

"What's on your mind?" Grace asks me.

"Nothing," I say.

I can feel her gaze on me, and I imagine she is taking in my wrinkles and all the age spots on my forehead, all those age spots dispersed around the perimeter of my hairline.

"I'm old," I tell her, forcing myself to laugh. "See the age spots?"

"Yes," she says. "Like petals along the fence of a garden."

"That's a good one," I say, and I turn to look at her. She appears to be scrutinizing my forehead, getting lost in it.

Embarrassed, I change the subject. "The river makes me think of fishing," I say. "It would be nice to one day go fishing."

"I don't know how," she says.

"I could teach you," I respond. I imagine us farther down the river, in a canoe maybe, with paddleboats and catamarans sharing the water with us. "We could hook all sorts," I tell her. "Walleye, crappies, bullheads, catfish, bass, even bluegills."

She turns her gaze to face the river. She tells me that she hardly recognizes those fish names. Catfish, she knows. Bluegills, too. The rest are new to her, she says. "It'd be nice to go fishing with you," she says.

It's a nice thought, us fishing together, me teaching her. I feel the rays of the sun on my shoulders, and I hear the distant quacking of the waterfowls. I look at her, and I think how nice it is to just sit here with her. This is enough, I think. Just this.

She clears her throat. And nothing prepares me for what she says next. "Have you ever been in love?" she asks.

"In love?" I ask.

"Really in love," she says, "the kind where every part of you feels like you could spend forever with the person. And you wish that forever could be more than a lifetime. The kind where you don't see all the things that are wrong with the person, all the negatives that should have prevented you from falling for the person in the first place."

"With love, you see the flaws," I tell her.

"Then that's what I mean," she says. "Only I wouldn't call them flaws."

I nod. "I suppose I was in love with my ex-husband," I say.

"And since then?" she asks. "How many years now, and you haven't fallen for anyone else?"

"People come and go," I say. "It's hard to find someone with whom you feel truly compatible."

"I've fallen in love," she tells me.

It shocks me, this confession of hers, and it scares me, too, and so I force myself not to look at her. "You've fallen in love?" I say, like an echo, and still I don't look at her.

"Yes," she says.

"It's not easy identifying love," I say.

"It's easy enough for me," she says. "Love is seeing someone the way God would see that person. Seeing in that person something pure and divinely beautiful, seeing in that person the true image of God."

"You're not God. You couldn't possibly know what it's like to see someone from the eyes of God." As I say it, I look up at her, and I examine her, as if examining will give me some clarity about what to feel. And it occurs to me that perhaps she is right. Because when I look at her, I see something all-beautiful in her, something all-perfect, if there ever was such a thing. Perhaps this is what God would see in us.

She crouches down in front of me, facing me. She is still holding her little box. She stoops on one knee and looks me in the eye and tells me how it's all wrong. She tells me that, beyond the fact that the Bible condemns that sort of love, she is almost certain that she'll not be good enough, that she couldn't possibly have experienced enough of the world to make it work, to rise to the level of the person she's fallen for. But that she's in love, and she's been trying to fight it, but she can't fight it anymore.

"You're getting married," I remind her. And I imagine the wedding, her mother tinkering with the wedding attire, fussing with the wrappers, placing the *jigida* beads just so. I imagine that I hear her mother's voice in the wedding hall, sharp and imperious, ordering Arinze around, telling him how to place the chairs, that sort of thing. I imagine Obinna's face, rough with stubble around the chin and cheeks. A man.

I imagine Grace running her fingers across his face, across his stubble, and I try to imagine her enjoying this, but I can't. I see his arms coming around her waist, I see her forcing her eyes shut, and when he is invited to kiss the bride, I imagine a stiff embrace, an awkward, lifeless peck.

I replace Obinna with myself. I imagine myself kissing her, and I imagine her leaning into me, running her fingers across my face, through my hair. And I feel myself aching. And I feel something like tears moistening my skin.

"You're getting married," I say again, in a whisper.

"I know," she says.

We don't say anything for a while, then she speaks, and the words gush out as if she's in a hurry to spill them. "You're much older, and I'm much younger," she says. Her voice is low, and there is a bit of a quiver in it. "One day, you'll begin to stoop, you might have to rely on a cane, and you'll lose your sight, your hearing, and maybe you'll even begin to lose your mind. And I will love you still. I'll love you the whole way through," she says. "I'll take care of you, bathe you, and water your grave with tears full of love. I know that I will."

I turn to look at her, because I believe her. And suddenly I'm extending my hand to slap her across her face, because I understand what she's telling me, and I understand that she's giving me permission to feel a way that I'm not sure I want the permission to feel. But her hand catches mine, as if she has read my mind.

"But then," she whispers, "who's to say that I won't die first? Who's to say that you won't be the one burying me?"

"Hush," I tell her, quietly, shaking my head, and I begin to sob.

As I kiss her, I don't think of the practical things, like what this will mean for my job, the scandal it might cause, the shame it might bring. I don't think of how I will explain all this to my daughter, to her husband, how they will explain it to their son. I don't think of all the affairs that I've witnessed in my twenty years at the university. I don't think of my disbelief at colleagues who held such distinguished positions at the university but allowed fleeting romances between themselves and their students to interfere with their careers. I don't think of any of this as we kiss.

And I don't think of the Bible, of its verses about unnatural affections and abominations. Because it doesn't feel sinful to me. Because none of this is meant to be a challenge to God.

Instead I relent in her arms and think of how good it feels—how nice her skin feels on mine. And I continue to taste her lips, plump and sweet. And I breathe in her fresh scent, flowery and light, like lavender.

She pulls away then, fusses with the gold ribbons on the red box, tugs the ribbons until they come undone. She reaches inside the box and takes out a small, round object in gold wrapping. "For you," she says to me. "A wedding favor," she says.

I reach out to accept. She places the object into my cupped hand, and then she covers my hand with her own. Our hands linger in midair that way, mine in hers. Then I pull away, because the whole thing feels not quite like a celebration—more like unadorned acceptance, just a bit short of joyful.

And I think that perhaps all this will do. The waterfowls are still quacking, and the sun is high in the sky. The river is still glowing in shades of silver and gold. Grace is sitting next to me, and I can't help thinking that perhaps the verge of joy is its own form of happiness.

JOHN KINSELLA

Penillion of James Ward's *Eye and Muzzle of a Cow* (Drawing)

Cow eyes swallow
The world's hollow
Places—the soul
You can't see lolls

Below surface,
Inside the curves
Of reflection
An inflection

Of seeing you,
And *watching* you
Searching, eye-deep,
Into the sleep

That will never
Come through the drawer
In which it rests,
So dark it tests

The quiet patience
Of the transfix-
ed single eye.
I spy and die.

But its muzzle
Sets right puzzles
Over tension,
Disconnection,

Seeming so calm,
Part of the psalm
Disembodied
On a thousand

Hills—lack of light
Keeping its tight
Color, keeping
Its *slow* breathing.

Penillion of Riding Past the Radio Astronomy Observatory Amid Hedges and Fields

Rabbits bolt back
Into the sack
Of shade, the gray
Penumbra may

Be a shelter
From space litter
Or some deep truth
Offering proof.

The sun is low
And hedge leaves blow
Red on the road.
Croak of a toad

Out of kilter
With cold's trigger:
Hibernation?
Observation

Of large and small
Arrays brings all
Cataclysms
And charisms

Into the range
Of rooks with strange
Penchants for glare
And curvature:

The dish hearing
Beyond the sing-
Song of the lone
Bird through the groans

Of the great flock
Flooding the track
Of light to dark,
To silence stark

As the traffic
Vanishes, marks
Revolutions
Of wheels and suns.

The sun is low
And hedge leaves blow
Red on the road.
Croak of a toad.

GREG WRENN

Fresco

To lose my father
I walked the road.

After a hot night of no wind.
One planet fading.

Withered orchard,
cloudy light.
A sprinkler, chugging
and returning.
Up to the right,
on a monastery wall, the face
of a frescoed saint,
all but a jawline
chipped away.
Initials scratched into
his faint bloodied gown. A fissure
across his book.

Burial

Scattering the relics
from my satchel,

I wandered scrubby hills.

A jay's song echoed
through boulders.

I placed his tongue,

white like wedding cake,
on a dry turkey-oak leaf.
To touch and be touched,

we've both entered rooms.
As his balls slapped

against someone, he prayed.

Just outside a tortoise burrow—
that's where I left his dick.

Wrinkled clown.

Rolled opiate.
Fallen toy pillar blazing

in the night at the end

of the century. At the edge
of those palmettos,

where I held a shovel.

Three Attempts to Understand Suffering

1.

A birdcall and a breath in the roofless chapel:
that pleasure was brief.

Unlike one full rotation of this galaxy.
Or sycamores peeling along the river,

guilt fanning out through my
body, is enlightenment accidental?

Like pear slice, dry mouth.

2.

This life—this one—
is a fleck of yolk
on a cooling skillet?

After so much,
I can rest?

3.

The ground under me damp
with early snowmelt, my
craving diminishes,

diminishes,
grows—die back,
return, die back,

die back—it surges
in my mind

toward a body other than his:
robins feeding; orange

breeds orange against
brown world. Snow only

at the north foot of

each tree. I'm dappled inside
with sunlight.

And then I'm not.

South of Jacksonville

Four shrimp boats on the horizon. Receding squall,
clear winter sea.
Walking the tide line,

I hear his voice again,

pained,
full of resolve.

The lagoon where
blue starfish flicker,

curl—I'll follow him there.

PETER LASALLE

The Manhattan Lunch: Two Versions

I. MAGAZINE GIRLS

For about a month after Hennessey was outright fired by the brokerage house, waiting to get what was sure to be the indictment from the federal court, he simply didn't go out much at all.

Most of the time Hennessey stayed in his spacious apartment on West Fifty-Fifth, and he made sandwiches for nearly all his meals, occasionally heading to one of the many reasonably priced restaurants on Ninth Avenue in the evening. On Ninth Avenue he would first walk some. He would maybe go to a place called El Deportivo that was Puerto Rican, nothing fancy, where along with the stewed *guisada* they gave you a choice of white or yellow rice and black or red beans (he always went for the yellow and black combination); or there was the Galaxy Café, where never taking one of the booths or the tables in back, Hennessey would sit at the diner-style counter more or less staring at the framed photographs of supposed entertainment celebrities there on the wall above the shelves of pies and cakes under glass (he wondered if anybody else his age, thirty-five, even re-membered anymore shaved-headed Telly Savalas, shown with his name scrawled prominently in one corner of the studio-lit shot). But when Hennessey found him-self paying at the Galaxy's cash register one evening and being told that because he had arrived before six he qualified for what they advertised with a window placard as the "Early Birdies' Special," he became self-conscious—after that, despite the decent meals there, he started avoiding the Galaxy altogether, if truth be known. Of course, he avoided news on the Internet and especially in the newspapers. The *Wall Street Journal*'s extensive coverage of the supposed financial scandal was painful to face, and much worse would be to pick up the floppy tabloid slab of the *Post* and possibly see (this happened once) his own name prominently mentioned in yet another piece concerning the "outrageous swindle" and it being a good ex-ample of the current "rampant greed," or that's what it was as far as the noisy *Post* was concerned.

He had played hockey in prep school (his father, a state-office clerical worker in Massachusetts, moonlighted weekends as a salesman in the appliance department of Sears to help pay the bills to send him to ritzy Milton Academy; his kind mother, so concerned that Hennessey do well in everything in life, always encouraged him even when his grades weren't all that good), true, he had played school hockey, though Hennessey certainly hadn't been of the caliber to play college-level, at Division III Bowdoin or anywhere else. Still, he liked hockey, and it got so that his evenings took on a pattern of watching all the televised Rangers games that winter, with the home ones broadcast from the Garden less than a couple of dozen blocks away. On some evenings he watched the pregame show and thought he might take a cab or even walk at a good clip down to the Garden to buy a twenty-five-buck ticket from one of the guys in hooded sweat shirts perpetually pedaling them outside; there was always an available seat, scalpers' surplus, when it was somebody of little consequence like the Phoenix or Vancouver team in town, but he never quite mustered the resolve for that.

He slept a lot, screened calls to make sure that it wouldn't be somebody from his family or whatever who might be offering more advice or condolences, neither of which Hennessey really needed. But one night at about nine he looked at the caller ID to see that it was Tom Bettencourt, an old pal from Bowdoin. Tom was somebody Hennessey had spent a lot of time with when they'd both first found themselves in New York after graduation, before Tom's marriage and his kids, and Hennessey did answer the ring, glad to hear Tom's sort of dry but laughing voice again. Automatically, Hennessey went through his side of the story on what had happened, though Tom really didn't seem to want to hear too much about that, which was refreshing. Then Hennessey asked Tom about his wife and kids, probably perfunctorily and part of the set protocol carried out by a bachelor when dealing with an old friend now married. Tom himself didn't seem to want to dwell on that either, and they just laughed some about guys they knew or girls they dated at Bowdoin or nearby Bates College, even the wonder of "Lobster Night" every other Sunday; with Bowdoin being right there in Brunswick, Maine—and, so, a ready supply of lobsters from the docks only miles away—a Bowdoin guy working his way through a bona fide pile of the red carcasses on a Sunday night plate oddly became a routine event.

"We got tired of lobster, can you imagine it?" Tom laughed.

"I can imagine it, all right," Hennessey said. "I used to have recurring nightmares about all those shells to be cracked, like it was so much endless work I had to do."

Which was how they both simply started agreeing that they surely should get together, it had been too long since they had. That also led to Hennessey learning that Tom Bettencourt wasn't working at the *New York Observer* anymore, but had moved to the staff of *Vanity Fair*; he was doing the same kind of editorial work he had done at the *Observer*, which involved some article assigning but mostly copyediting. Tom suggested that with the building for Condé Nast located so close to where Hennessey lived—it being right off Times Square, a new skyscraper with the distinctive rounded-off edge to just one corner of its facade at Forty-Second Street—they should have lunch at the Condé Nast commissary. Tom assured Hennessey the scene there was worth seeing, and, granted, though it was only a cafeteria, this was an exceptionally posh one and designed by the very famous postmodern architect, a guy who had done major museum buildings and such throughout the world but whose name Hennessey didn't recognize; plus, as Tom added: "It can be a real trip, the scene there, because it serves all the magazines the company owns, us and *The New Yorker* and the rest. And if we're real lucky we'll see some of the models from *Vogue*, who come to the building for meetings to discuss shoots, I guess, even come for the actual studio shoots somewhere in the building. And I'm talking supermodels, man—certified Grade A and then some, if you know what I mean."

Hennessey laughed, and while he was still fully aware that Tom had indeed brushed aside any mention whatsoever from Hennessey about his current problems, Hennessey knew that he, Hennessey, was *very* comfortable with, and therefore appreciative of, that brushing aside, if only done out of politeness on Tom's part—or perhaps because of the fact that their friendship had nothing to do with Hennessey's current serious problems, really.

Nevertheless, Hennessey nearly backed out of the lunch at the last minute. He rehearsed a couple of excuses to make, because on Monday of the week when they were supposed to meet on Thursday, Hennessey had gone to Lower Manhattan to talk with his lawyers again, a session that hadn't gone well at all. But on the Thursday—a very gray midday with that almost ammonia smell of possible snow in the cold February air—he walked on Fifty-Fifth over to Broadway and headed into Times Square, past the theaters and to the sleek skyscraper—bone-white stone and tinted glass—that housed the Condé Nast operations. He had to go through extensive security, all right, and the guy in the blue blazer standing at one of the upright reception desks—there were several, like an airport-counter operation—called up to Tom at the *Vanity Fair* offices and then issued Hennessey a pass with his name on it, printed out right there, the guy instructing Hennessey to keep ahold of it and directing him to the particular elevator in the long row of them that served the floor he needed. Hennessey folded the sheet, tucked it in his sheepskin car coat's pocket.

Tom Bettencourt wore slacks, an open-collar striped dress shirt, and chocolate suede desert boots, no suit jacket; his tuft of red hair was still wild as ever, but now, somewhat moonfaced, Tom looked decidedly heavier, more of the father that he was, maybe, since the last time Hennessey had seen him (Tom had two young kids, both boys). As it turned out they didn't head right to the commissary, but went on an impromptu tour of the offices, which admittedly Hennessey found interesting, not quite what he had expected. Actually, the place was rather empty, quiet, with a sequence of white-walled rooms uniformly carpeted in tasteful dark blue, the furniture just black steel desks and chrome-and-black-leather chairs; Tom explained that the editor in charge now—the guy who had brought Tom with him to the magazine from the *Observer*—was a minimalist at heart and had the whole place redone that way. There was one interesting room where all the mock-ups for the pages for the upcoming issue—entire articles and advertising layout—were lined up in sequence on lit electronic panels around the white walls, strung like boxcars, and then there was Tom's own small office. It was white-walled like all the rest, and Tom, obviously proud, showed Hennessey a literary journal that came out of some Midwestern university in which he had recently published a short story. With his wise-guy laugh, Tom informed Hennessey that he still hoped to finish a novel and publish it, doing something significant with real literature, rather than—he loopingly waved his hand while sitting there in his chair and leaning back from the bare black steel desk, as if to take in the whole operation of *Vanity Fair*—yes, rather than what was around him: "All this yuppie horseshit of slick magazine writing, the glitz and high-class gossip that *Vanity Fair* is really all about, you know."

At which point Tom got up and said it was time to eat, the two of them taking an elevator down several floors to the commissary. Tom nodded hello to a couple of people they passed in the offices on the way out, also exchanged talk with somebody in the elevator.

The commissary was as thoroughly dramatic as promised, a true expanse with some smaller private rooms off the main concourse and easily a couple of hundred people eating at the tables arranged in clusters, restaurant-style. The colors were bright, all oranges and blues, and the free-form panels of the undulating dividing walls suggested giant futuristic bird wings, maybe, seeming to flap their way along beneath the glowing inset lights up top that looked like stars against the high ceiling's very black background. Yet the more impressive show was probably not in the design within by the famous architect (who in this assignment, Hennessey told himself, appeared to be trying altogether too hard) but there at the table Tom selected for its view. The skyscraper's side was glass here, and outside, seemingly close enough to touch, was the panorama of Bryant Park behind the ornate rise of the Public Library—the feathery, winter-bare trees of the park, also its paved terraces and its walkways and its many benches; everything in the winter day was rendered a mesmerizing underwater hue due to the tinting of the huge glass sheets that formed the sweep of the building's facade at this level relatively lower down, four or five floors above the street. They talked about how good the food was, just cream soup and pita sandwiches for both of them, but *quite* good, they talked more about what they read about Bowdoin lately in the alumni magazine, so much new construction there and also Bowdoin's genuine track star, a sprinter somehow recruited from Jamaica, an acknowledged hotbed for sprinters, somebody who had nearly made it, believe or not, to the summer Olympics for his country the year before; they talked of a lot of small things, and Hennessey had to admit that for the first time in who knows how long he was feeling something close to relaxed.

All of which is to say, that made what happened all the more strange when it did happen. Because when there was an actual nudge from Tom's desert boot under the table to signal Hennessey that about to enter were two of the sort of models he had mentioned on the phone, "magazine girls" and definitely from *Vogue*, Hennessey did look that way, watched the pair of models come from a smaller dining room off the main concourse and make their way to the front doors, having finished whatever meal of probably a simple salad and iced tea that they had merely poked away at.

Both were tall, willowy at five-ten or so, and the one with ash-blond hair, mile-high cheekbones, and the mandatory pout, she wore just casual jeans and a sweater; the other, with a glossy black pageboy cut so straight in bangs that it could have been done using a steel rule to guide the scissors, such full lips, she was dressed equally casually, loose corduroy slacks in her case with a sweater—both wore pristine running shoes, most likely taking a break from a shoot. They were undeniably and entirely lovely, bordering on ethereal, with that rhythmic strut that fashion models never really abandon, whether it be entering a bar in the

Hamptons in the summer—as Hennessey had come to learn from his own carefree seaside summers renting a fine beach house there with bachelor pals—or now simply leaving a cafeteria—shoulders alternatingly swaying, perfect posture and the long, long legs seemingly a couple of paces ahead of them, almost as if each of the girls were leaning back to hold an imaginary pooch tugging her along on a leash. Yes, Hennessey looked at them as he sat at the table, the clutter of dishes from the meal in front of him, he looked at the girls—and he simply started crying, full-fledged, hunch-shouldered sobbing, pretty loud.

Tom at first must have thought Hennessey was joking around, and then—as Hennessey didn't let up and people at other tables nearby were, in fact, looking their way—Tom seemed to just want to be the hell out of there. Hennessey, still crying, mumbled something about how absolutely *beautiful* they were, and Tom, speaking low and with a touch of detectable anger—as more people at other tables were definitely looking at them now, it was embarrassing—Tom finally said to Hennessey at the table, "What the fuck is the matter with you, man?"

Everything was quite awkward as Hennessey, composed again, and Tom parted ten minutes later, uneasily shaking hands down in the lobby.

The next week Hennessey tried calling Tom Bettencourt a couple of times, leaving messages both at his office and at home that weren't returned. And by the following week Hennessey was busy and he had no time for something like calls to Tom Bettencourt right then, with the indictment about to come down at last. Or perhaps Hennessey convinced himself that Tom Bettencourt, who aspired to publishing short stories in literary journals of the flimsily bound variety that he had showed Hennessey in the office—journals of no consequence that surely nobody really read—wasn't worth dealing with, would never amount to much in life.

Truth of the matter was that Hennessey suddenly was *very* busy.

His head lawyer told Hennessey that he, the lawyer, would need to meet with him personally several times more that week before the upcoming two sessions for Hennessey with the prosecuting lawyers and investigators, one staff of them from the state attorney general's office and then the other with the federal Securities and Exchange Commission, the latter pushing for considerable prison time.

II. FALLING INTO PAINTINGS

Hope's life at seventy-eight had its understandable routine. There was time with her one daughter Anne, living up in Larchmont, and the two grandchildren, also

Hope's considerable reading and the so-called appreciation courses she took, sponsored by Columbia.

Which is how it happened.

Actually, the worst thing about it all was the coverage that started turning up everywhere, the attention compounding and lasting for a full few days. First on the local New York news and then, apparently, on various news websites, a compact version of what happened provided by a wire service.

At her age Hope didn't know what to think of attention like that.

She wasn't what her adult daughter Anne or anybody else would consider very media savvy, not by any means. And for Hope, more than simply fainting that way in the course of the lecture for her seniors' art appreciation course there in the Metropolitan Museum of Art and hitting the painting's sheened canvas, which ripped badly in the course of the collapse, yes, more than that was the whole certainly odd adventure of being rushed by the wailing yellow and blue ambulance van right down Fifth Avenue. They sped beside the park with its surely winter-bare trees, then swerved across town on maybe Fifty-Seventh—and this she distinctly remembered—the two muscular EMS attendants in their dark-blue jumpsuits occasionally looking down at her and smiling as she lay stretched out like that, both, comically, with identical trimmed moustaches; one was talking to the other about where they were heading on this particular run, Saint Clare's near Times Square, which they apparently had nicknamed the "junkie hospital." She was out of the emergency room by seven that evening, all tests proving she was fine, in truth quite fit for a woman of seventy-eight years old, the peachy-cheeked young intern told her. Her daughter Anne showed up from the suburbs in Anne's husband's Saab wagon to drive her back to her apartment on the Upper East Side, in what used to be known as Yorkville. Anne wanted to stay for the night, but Hope assured her there was nothing wrong, even tried to make a joke out of the whole thing by saying she had no idea why those attendants called Saint Clare's the junkie hospital, demeaning it that way, seeing that to her everybody there had seemed professional, attentive, and efficient, especially the boyish intern who, when asked, told Hope in detail all about how his own parents in New Jersey had sacrificed a lot to send him through Albert Einstein for medical school.

The phone started ringing that evening, when a cousin in Connecticut had first seen the short TV squib of the story showing the museum gallery and the large

Delacroix canvas, which, as Hope had already been assured by everybody at the hospital, could be repaired easily enough, despite the vertical rip being quite long; then later that evening there was Ray Finelli, the Columbia grad student conducting the class for her group, yes, cheery Ray telling her the same; then another call from Anne who was obviously excited, it now appeared, that her mother had become the object of such celebrity. Anne called again in the morning when she heard the story about the torn painting and what had happened to her mother being given mention on the morning NPR news, which Hope regularly listened to but was intentionally avoiding when she did get up and begin to prepare her coffee and juice and toast at her usual seven o'clock.

Hope had no caller ID on her one phone, in the living room, but there was a cheap and basic answering machine that Anne had bought for her at Duane Reade a dozen years ago and that Hope often did switch off even when she had no specific problem to deal with and before this happened, wanting to protect her time to read; lately Anne had wanted to buy her a cell phone, but Hope didn't like the idea of it—too many interruptions when you maybe were, in fact, somewhere trying to relax and read a book. And after a second call came from Anne that morning and then three other calls from various people in the art appreciation class for seniors—Gladys Revotskie and Mary Torrey and Julia Heyman—Hope grew tired of having to explain it all again, telling yet somebody else how she had been assured the damage could be repaired—which had seemed foremost in her own mind while at the hospital, not any question of her health—and also telling whoever was calling how the young intern at Saint Clare's said it must have happened because she had skipped lunch that day. The intern decided it was a matter of simple blood-sugar level and it could happen to anybody, even somebody his age. She had told him, when asked, that she had eaten some rye crisp, cottage cheese, and a slice of Plumrose ham for lunch at about eleven before she met with her group in the lobby of the Met that afternoon, which was, actually, her normal meal at midday; nevertheless, the cheery young intern, thinking that it was much less than she usually ate, immediately concluded almost with an "Aha!" that she had picked the wrong day to do what he saw as "skip lunch." Hope herself knew it had had nothing to do with blood-sugar level.

But in a way, not talking on the phone and not being occupied with some conversation was probably worse, because it gave her too much time to think about the incident, let the slow, emphatically full-color reel of it—after all, this was *Delacroix*—play itself out again on what could have been the big screen of her imagination. Everything had started off normally enough: Hope noticing the usual few yellow school buses parked out front of the Met in the gray of the February day, Hope walking up the long rise of steps and, at the doors, past those glass canisters filled with the little metal entry tabs that they tell you to deposit for recycling on your way out, Hope at the coatroom checking her winter coat with her gloves and knit hat carefully pushed into the pocket, keeping her red handbag in which she had a small pad and pens in case she wanted to take notes, and then Hope meeting the bunch of others from the appreciation class at the far end of the massive lobby by the bookstore. Grinning Ray Finelli in his graduate student's black jeans and black turtleneck herded them together as if he were a conscientious grade school teacher, Ray laughing, always pleasant, amid all those voices of the many museumgoers echoing around the big white marble pillars and along the lobby's high white marble walls; it was something Hope always liked, the bustle and palpable excitement of a museum lobby—the *anticipation* of what's to come. The lecture from Ray that day was on the nineteenth-century painting in France that had laid the groundwork for the two great movements that eventually marked, as he explained, the latter part of that century—Impressionism and Symbolism. And while they did find themselves in a gallery with dark-green walls showing a half-dozen Corots and Millets, smallish and more or less uniformly murky, the mishap happened when the bunch of them were standing there and listening to Ray talk right in front of the huge and decidedly vivid Delacroix canvas. It was the scene of a sultan and his warriors, in turbans and robes and with the horses' jeweled, gleaming harnesses and saddles flashing as brightly as the Moors' scimitars themselves, preparing perhaps for battle in front of the golden walls of a medina; the Moroccan sky was so big and so blue above it all that just to look at it was enough to make you dizzy on its own, near overwhelming in its richness and also its trueness—the essence of something that you really couldn't name, or probably well beyond naming, which made it that much more, yes, true and rich and, undeniably, an *essence*. Ray Finelli was still talking, the dozen or so of them were listening attentively, Hope was looking at that blue sky—and the next thing Hope knew everybody was gathered and looking down at her as she lay there tangled like a dropped puppet on the honey parquet floor and against the dark-green wall, finally opening her eyes, blinking. She would later decide that it must have been her elbow that hit the thin, taut canvas and caused the damage on the way down.

Actually, thinking too much about it, she did turn on the answering machine again in hopes that somebody *would* call, and at four, when Anne's twin daughters were home from junior high, they took turns on the phone, wanting to make sure themselves that she, "Gram," was all right; like their mother, they apparently were a bit excited, too, saying they had told all the other kids about it at school and to "check it out" on the Web.

The third day was little different, more calls, including two from reporters. Now that she thought of it, Hope was surprised the reporters hadn't contacted her earlier; one was from a large New York all-news radio station and one from a weekly newspaper in Brooklyn that Hope admittedly had never heard of. Both reporters sounded quite young and with both she was polite, avoiding making any more comment, and no sooner did she finish with the second call than she answered another ring, Ray Finelli phoning again. He reassured her not to worry, saying once more it was amazing what restorers could do with canvas damage nowadays and emphasizing that the Met, of course, had "humongous insurance" for this kind of thing, not to worry whatsoever; however, he said that at some point she would probably have to file a more complete report with the museum people—he would keep her informed. But by the fourth day the phone had quieted at last, and when it did ring late in the morning she listened to the prerecorded greeting that came with the answering machine say with its packaged, game-show-announcer's voice, even-toned, "We are not home now" and the rest of it (Anne had explained to Hope even before the museum incident that, for security, it wasn't a good idea to give as much as your first name or any sort of personal greeting message on a machine); there followed a message with a male's voice, a little raspy and older-sounding, first saying he hoped he had the right number, and then identifying himself as Dan Sorensen, somebody who, as he said, he hoped that she remembered after so many years. She looked at the little green light on the black phone flashing rhythmically in the course of the message being taken, and she picked up the receiver before he was finished:

"Dan?"

"Hope?"

And they began talking, as naturally as that. She hadn't heard from Dan Sorensen for who knows how long, it amazingly being close to a full sixty years, they eventually decided with some extended calculation, as they laughed and talked about so many things, Dan explaining that he had seen the news squib and simply looked up her number in the phone book. There was so much to be covered, so much to be talked about, though once the family material got filled in—Hope telling how her husband Norman had died ten years earlier, her one daughter Anne and Anne's husband the investment banker had two wonderful girls, twins, living in Westchester, and Dan talking of having survived two wives, no children, admitting that probably his work as a civil engineer when younger, with considerable travel to Europe and South America for that work, never let him think about starting a family until it was too late to do so—yes, once all that was out of the way, even the explanation of how Dan himself lived not far from her and on the Upper West Side, had lived there for years after his retirement, everything did return to talk of when they had been boyfriend and girlfriend during their last year in high school. Or, high school for Dan, anyway, and the girls' Catholic day school on the Upper East Side for Hope—what they used to call an "exclusive" school and run by the Order of the Sacred Heart nuns, originally French.

"You know," Dan now said, "I knew when you first told me back then that you had decided to go to that even ritzier women's college, a place with that same order of swank nuns up there in the suburbs, your Manhattanville College, my days were numbered, all right, that it was only a matter of months or even days before you would meet some guy from some place like Harvard." But then he seemed to question himself on that, an inadvertent addendum: "And it was Harvard for your husband Norman?"

"He went to Yale, actually."

"I guess I always thought it was Harvard."

"No, both of Norman's degrees, for college and then law school, were from Yale."

"What's the difference, way out of my league in either case," Dan laughed, and Hope did, too.

They ended up talking for well over an hour, while neither of them seemed to notice the time, and there was more laughing, more remembering, Hope sitting there in her apartment's living room and somehow not sitting there whatsoever, just picturing places that came up in the conversation, like a slow slide show, just picturing people and especially picturing Dan—square-jawed and handsome when they had been together when young, his thick mahogany hair carefully parted on one side the way boys groomed their hair back then and the large blue eyes that, true, often made him look perfectly startled, perhaps with life itself; sunburnt Tom in khakis and canvas shoes and a crew-neck sweater, a refreshingly cool summer evening after a fine day at the beach for the two of them out on Long Island in Hope's precise picturing now—and soon, on the phone, they were agreeing

75

to meet for lunch the next week, that somehow happening without Hope even noticing it, she later told herself.

And all the following weekend Hope also told herself that thinking about Dan now, plus once or twice mentioning him and the upcoming lunch to her daughter Anne, she seemed to forget altogether what had happened in the museum on the gray afternoon less than a full week before. It would be good to see Dan again, which is what Hope kept telling herself that weekend, wondering what Dan looked like today, wondering what he would think she looked like today, wondering about just about everything concerning Dan and probably excited, though she wouldn't fully admit that. It went on all Saturday and Sunday, right until Monday—when Dan did call again; he was laughing, despite what he had to tell her, sounding boyish and the voice no longer strange or raspy, the way it had been when she had first heard it unidentified on the earlier call and he had begun to leave his message. Dan explained now that he would have to ask for "the old Yankees-game rain check" on the lunch, and the doctor he had seen that very morning wanted him to book into the hospital immediately, Mount Sinai, for some tests: "One thing I forgot to mention when we talked the other day, Hopey"—she wondered when somebody had last called her Hopey? her mother, her own three sisters? all now dead—"I've had a lot of problems with my ticker these last few years, they rope me in for these tests all the time. So, a rain check it will be, OK, Hopey?"

"Yes," Hope said, rather softly, saying repeatedly that she surely hoped it all worked out OK.

Dan Sorensen died during heart surgery at Mount Sinai that Thursday. Hope went to the funeral services at the Catholic church on Columbus Avenue the following Monday, attended by only a dozen people, mostly retired elderly colleagues who had known him from work. But she didn't go up to the burial at Woodlawn in the Bronx, even though the kind, polite Hispanic priest had offered to let her come with him in his car, saying he could drop her off at her apartment on the way back; she admitted to the young priest that she was quite tired, and he said he understood.

As sorrowful as it had been, she was appreciative that she had at least talked to Dan before he passed away, and she was appreciative that they had shared for at least that hour of phone conversation the memories of other times. And by that spring, April and then May, Hope was back to her routine of reading and spending time with her grandchildren, with the whole idea of her moment of celebrity entirely behind her, that day when she had fallen into the canvas; Hope was looking forward to receiving the printed schedule from Columbia of appreciation courses for seniors for the coming academic year, thinking she might sign up for one in literature this time.

In other words, Hope's life returned, very much so, to its normal routine, except for the strangest part of it all, the dreams she kept having night after night, it seemed, in which she was always falling into—sometimes tumbling into and sometimes leaning into and sometimes full-fledged being swept along for a collision with the canvas about to tear—Hope falling into so many paintings of so many artists she did know because their work was very famous—falling into Monet's feathery pastels and those giant water lilies, and falling into Whistler's obliquely named "Symphonies" and "Nocturnes," and, almost humorously, it seemed, falling into Grant Wood's stony-faced Iowa farmer and his wife, pitchfork held upright like a staff, several Mondrians and Picassos, too—and also falling into paintings she had never known or never heard of, with such a variety of frames encasing them, all of which Hope seemed to remember from the dreams, distinctly, those frames, some frilled gold and ornate, some brushed stainless steel and starkly minimal, and who could calculate just how *many* paintings all told—and Hope perpetually falling.

In the morning Hope, having her coffee and juice and toast, would try to recall which paintings they were, what exactly it was she had fallen into this time, if, in fact, she had had another dream like that the night before.

On the other hand, maybe Hope didn't think of any such dreaming whatsoever (*had she actually once fallen into that big, vivid Delacroix canvas of swashbuckling Moorish warriors atop their fine steeds that winter day at the Met? did anybody ever actually fall into a painting as she had, literally, and had there been the odd few days of celebrity for Hope that February before, then the whole even more odd business of the call out of the blue from Dan Sorensen after all these years? had that happened? or had that been a dream, too? she wasn't so sure anymore*), no, maybe she didn't think of any of it any longer, and it was merely a matter of Hope knowing more than ever now what she had already come to quietly accept.

Because it was true—Hope was getting *close*.

MAGGIE SMITH

Marked

They are alone, the woman and the girl child.
The man has gone over the mountain

to work for a year, maybe longer, and the sunlight
here is a little bitter, the color of turmeric,

the same gold as the leaves floating down.
The girl has an eye like a spyglass for birds.

She must be marked, the woman thinks.
Wherever she walks, the shadow of a hawk

falls on her, the way a light trains on something.
In this thick forest, light can't touch

every leaf, but the woman watches
wind touch all of them. If they weren't paper-

thin, this rustling would be a hammering
like hooves on hard ground. The man will return,

but what a strange homecoming to the world
belonging to the woman and child. They cut

its intricate shapes from nothing, like silhouettes
from paper. They have a rhythm. Mornings

to the creek on horseback, ocher leaves
falling through ocher air nearly indistinguishable.

Evenings, at the fire, telling stories the man
won't know. Maybe there is something about

his hands, rough as bark, the girl will remember.
But if she's grown wild in this wilderness,

who could blame her. Once small enough
to fit inside the hawk's fallen shadow,

now she can almost outrun it, only the dark
blade of a wingtip scissoring across her face.

The Hawk

The hawk has never seen a girl child.
This new creature—smaller than a fawn,

song unlike a bird's—hushes the air
with her gold hair. The clearing seems

an invitation to light her, but the hawk
has no light to shine, only shadow.

He hovers, training his own dark double
on the girl. They are tethered, an invisible

string between them. She rarely speaks
but sings. The hawk has never seen notes

shaped like hers, each one an empty
locket with space inside it, but for what?

This is not for birds to understand.
The hawk loves the girl child best

in the open, only sunlight strumming
the tether between them, her notes

rising easily to him the way an echo
homes to the voice that calls it.

The Hunters

The hunters are just passing through.
The three men stop to rest,

to dip their ladles in the cold creek,
and there are the woman

and the girl child. The girl wears
the shadow of a hawk, feathers

like a fine-printed fabric on her skin.
The men don't know what to make

of the bird, how it hovers above her
as if held aloft by an undercurrent.

On the hillside, the lit tents glow
like lanterns. The hunters wonder

if this place is real, if they will find
their way back here and see nothing

but trees—no girl, no hawk,
no woman, no metallic cold rusting

their tongues, no spell of these woods
to be broken. But tonight the men

are warm, fed, their coarse hair cut,
their horses heaped with furs,

and the woman wears firelight
on her face, the paper lace of the dark

flickering—a reminder of the soft,
bewitching world inside the world.

Nest

For nesting, the hawk gathers the girl's
long hair—glinting, caught in a low branch,

snagged on a clothesline. Soon he'll look
for her gold curls, almost transparent

in the light, and see strands the color of bark,
dull and dark and straight. Sycamores

shed their roughest skin to reveal
the color of milk. Is the girl like this,

becoming again and again what she was
when the hawk first spied her—young,

shining like a broken bit of mirror
on the ground? The hawk doesn't know

this is a human story, the girl's story
he is only a small part of. High in a pine

is a soft, blond nest of baby hair.

Storybook

Elsewhere in this world there is water
you cannot see beyond, the hunters say,

and seabirds. The men say the ocean
is not so far from here, and the more

they say it, the more the girl smells salt
on the piney air. Elsewhere in this world

is water you cannot cross on horseback
or raft, but this place is all tinder

and leaves, all paper like a book cracked
open on its spine, and these mountains,

this intricate forest, cut from its pages.
The girl wonders if this is what the crows

have been doing with their sharp cries:
cutting leaf shapes from paper, cutting

their own shadows to throw down,
cutting the hawk's so it can follow her.

She wonders if when a baby is born
on this mountain, a caw cuts the child's

shape from flesh, too. The girl
could be elsewhere in this world, but here

she has a long, dark girl to lie down beside.

Splinter

The man returns, beard thick and rough
as splintered wood, and finds what he feared:

the woman happy, the blond baby
he left now a dark-haired girl.

He knows hunters passed through;
the girl has a fox fur the color of rust.

The woman must have been lonely.
She must have worn her hair—the color

of a copper kettle—with one loose tendril
at the nape of her neck. The firelight

must have come alive on her skin.
Now she comes in alone from the pasture

at night, raised lantern swaying. She lies
a long time with the child, whisper-singing

some lullaby he's never heard into her hair.
This side of the mountain isn't home

anymore. In the morning, as the man splits
logs for the fire, a long splinter stitches

itself into the tender meat of his palm.
He dips his hand into the cold creek

and watches the water cloud with blood,
then run clear, as if he had never been there.

Mountain Child

When the girl leaves the mountain,
she is no longer a child,

but she has not outgrown the hawk.
She wears its shadow on her shoulder,

an epaulet. It bears the weight
of allegory. When the girl leaves

the mountain, it's autumn,
so many yellow leaves on the gingko,

clusters of butterflies seem to cling
to each branch. Each time

the wind blows, a few take wing.
When the girl leaves, the mountain

flickers with shadows. What else
can left-behind birds offer

but their own shapes cut
from the papery dark. They call, *Please,*

girl child, mountain child. The ground
beneath her feet is a trick

of gold wings—at any moment a few
might flutter, then rise all at once.

ALISON ROSSITER

Artist's Statement

THE DARKROOM IS ESSENTIAL to my work process as a photographer, whether it involves traditional methods or experimentation. I have worked with the materials and processes of light-sensitive, gelatin-silver-based photography since 1970. Recently, two years spent volunteering at the Sherman Fairchild Photographic Conservation laboratory at the Metropolitan Museum of Art immersed me in the field of photograph conservation and fed my deep interest in the history of photographic materials.

As technology evolves, so does my interest in materiality. Working without a camera or negatives in the darkroom led me to experiment with using a flashlight to draw on light-sensitive photographic paper. This created bold geometric abstractions. My light drawings series *Light Horse* and *Dark Horse*, from which this portfolio is assembled, grew from my lifelong admiration of horses. This admiration spurred a desire to draw representational images. I am a photographer, so this was foreign territory. As I created these light drawings, what I discovered was the beauty of the magnificent tones of silver gelatin that only exist through the basic photographic processes of light and chemistry.

After the light drawings, I began to explore the possibility of finding latent images in long-forgotten packages of expired black-and-white photographic papers. Atmospheric conditions, pollutants, light leaks, and physical damage can cause changes in the light-sensitive properties of these photographic papers. I process these sheets of paper in my darkroom to reveal found photograms. I have collected over twelve hundred individual packages of paper with expiration dates that represent the photographic industry of the late nineteenth century and every decade of the twentieth century. When I process these papers, they yield abstract images that bear a surprising resemblance to artworks from the last century. Each print title contains three facts: the manufacturer and type of paper, the expiration date on the package, and the date that I processed the material.

ALISON ROSSITER
Light Horse, 2003
light drawing on gelatin silver paper, 16 x 20 in.
Courtesy Stephen Bulger Gallery

ALISON ROSSITER
Light Horse (Buck), 2006
light drawing on gelatin silver paper, 8 x 10 in.
Courtesy Stephen Bulger Gallery

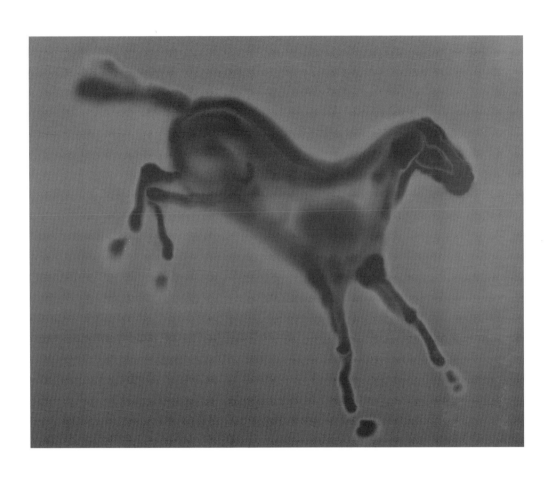

ALISON ROSSITER
Dark Horse (Buck), 2006
light drawing on gelatin silver paper, 8 x 10 in.
Courtesy Stephen Bulger Gallery

ALISON ROSSITER
Light Horse Head, 2003
light drawing on gelatin silver paper, 8 x 10 in.
Courtesy Stephen Bulger Gallery

ALISON ROSSITER
Light Horse No. 6, 2003
light drawing on gelatin silver paper, 8 x 10 in.
Courtesy Alison Rossiter

ALISON ROSSITER
Light Horse (Buck), 2006
light drawing on gelatin silver paper, 8 x 10 in.
Courtesy Stephen Bulger Gallery

ALISON ROSSITER
Light Horse (Buck), 2006
light drawing on gelatin silver paper, 8 x 10 in.
Courtesy Stephen Bulger Gallery

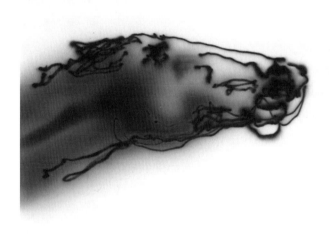

ALISON ROSSITER
Light Horse Head, 2003
light drawing on gelatin silver paper, 8 x 10 in.
Courtesy Stephen Bulger Gallery

SUSAN LAUGHTER MEYERS

Not one single further sorrow

here, where this morning three horses nuzzled
at the fence near the gravel road,
their chestnut heads and necks glistening—

here, where I could forget sorrow
and how the young girl from our class that summer
gave up on herself, and the news spread quickly.

Or, if not a forgetting, a diminishment—the way the horizon
across the field of grasses and bachelor's buttons
softens its line to a fringe of blossoms and stems.

This title and the line quoted in the poem that follows are from *If Not, Winter: Fragments of Sappho*, translated by Anne Carson.

[Let's say you forgot me]

Let's say you forgot me—
no, not forgot: were unable to reach,
one of us out of the country,
say, me this time
writing in France. I put down line
after line, shapes anyone could make
something out of,
black ink on cream paper, waiting for you
to call. Your phone, my phone,
somebody's phone isn't working.
My thoughts are growing remote,
and the words come to me
in a language I can't translate.
Weeks pass, as weeks will do.
My handwriting becomes illegible
and the ink is starting to fade.

DAVID MOOLTEN

Stillbirth

They cleaned and dressed it, showed it to her arms,
Half a bread loaf, a large potato,
The pathetic little body perfect
And complete, its ten fingers evolved from stars.
She lets his inertia crawl upon her,
A drowned boy pulled from her waters,
A Donatello bambino, all marble
And no pulse, a swift pietà. The days
Have drifted into months of twilit wonder.
The shuddering never ends, a stuffed panda,
Blue paint cans, Hans Christian Andersen.
For her, it's reflex, this pushing away—
For others, who don't call, change the subject,
Safe distance from taboo. She's the one,
The jackpot winner struck by lightning,
The sacrificial virgin in whose ear
The angel mouthed his promise then took it back,
The poor girl handed a hand-me-down doll,
Her son so good, so quiet, even the state
Treats him as a do-over, a false start,
Nothing on file despite her full breasts.
He starves for context, his name the whole legend,
A lie of omission, a placeholder,
A brief lull in the conversation.

CHARD DENIORD

Under the Sun

The days are my consolation.
I take one home each night
and put it in the case beside
my bed and watch it fade
in the dark, no matter how shiny
it seems at first, no matter how high
it stands behind the glass. I keep
a few polished for memory's sake,
but even they grow tarnished
and lost among the others.
"Thank you," I say to the dusk
each night for another trophy
engraved with the cloud code
of that particular day—April 10,
June 19 . . . As for the diamond-
studded chalice I glimpsed in a dream,
I no longer want it, although I live
as if I do to fool myself, throwing
quarters at a wall, playing
the numbers, singing, "Grief is happy
with a stone. See how bright
it shines on the dull cold ground."

Smooth Dark Stone

Already I know from the smooth dark stone

that a name disappeared in time and the weather.

How to carve another for now as deep

as the other and not believe it will last forever?

STEVEN HARVEY

The Vanishing Point

W OODY HERMAN'S MUSIC is sweeping the nation," my mother wrote in 1945, and Kansas City, where she and Dad went to college, was a jazz hub. One year before they had married, my parents—Max and Bobbie—were dating and caught up in a swirl of Kansas City activities: shopping, going to shows, dancing all night in clubs. Dad drove and they often bounced from town to town following the music and twisting to "the boogie." Sometimes they stopped along the way for picnics where Dad cooked steaks over a wood fire. In a letter dated October 7, 1945, one of many she wrote to my grandmother throughout her life, my mother describes an all-nighter filled with excitement and music. It began with a trip to Topeka where Dad bought "a beautiful brown suit" and my mother purchased "a black slip and bra, good white scarf, and a black purse." She was ready for a night on the town: "At last I have my outfit."

They drove to Lawrence to pick up their friends, Neal and Shirley, at the bus station, and headed off for "KC," arriving about six. "We stopped at the Interlude," and "had steaks and listened to Joshua Johnson," who played piano boogie.

The main event though was Woody Herman. "He's Coming," the newspaper clipping that fell out of the envelope of one of my mother's letters announced, "The Country's Greatest Dance Band." Herman would be in Kansas City "for one night" in his "only Midwest appearance." His orchestra included Frances Wayne, as the vocalist, and other "stars" of the jazz scene: Chubby Jackson, Flip Phillips, and Bill Harris.

My parents and their friends arrived at the municipal auditorium about eight thirty. "It is a huge building one block square," my mother wrote, agog. They worked their way through the crowd to the front of the room, "right below the stage," and were there when the musicians "took their places." In 1945, Woody Herman's star was on the rise. He and his orchestra, called "The Herd," had just signed a contract with Columbia, recording hits like "Laura" and "Caldonia." The next year Herman played Carnegie Hall and won awards from *Billboard*, *Metronome*, and *Esquire* as the top band in the country. My mother's reaction was mixed. The musicians "were peculiar looking" and Herman's style was too flashy for her taste. "Even on sweet and mellow pieces he always has to end it up with jump and jive." She preferred the more conventional sound of Les Brown, but admitted that the musicians in Herman's band "sure could play" and that the audience was "wild about it."

The room was too crowded for dancing. "We stood there jammed against the stage for two hours," my mother complained. "Finally Shirley & I could stand it no longer because our feet were killing us." The two of them went to the balcony and watched from there until 12:45 AM when the band stopped. By the time the concert was over, all of the restaurants in the city were "jammed with people" so they headed to Lawrence to drop off Neal and Shirley, eating in Ottawa, a town along the way, and talking until four thirty in the morning. "We had to talk fast and furious to keep awake." Later they ate a breakfast in Wamego and reached Manhattan at eight o'clock where my dad dropped off my mother on his way to start work, without sleep, at nine.

"What happened to the woman I married?" my dad once asked. My stepmother mentioned the question while we were sorting old photos at her house in Kentucky last year. It was a conversation that she and my dad had when they first met in Saint Louis in 1959 or 1960, consoling each other for the messes that their marriages had become, and it's a good question. My mother clearly was attracted to the excitement that my dad offered. She liked a pretty outfit with a black purse and fancy undergarments, danced the boogie-woogie, stayed up all night to hear jazz, ate steak dinners, "had more fun"—as in the phrase "we had more *fun*"—at the show "*Anchors Aweigh*," clowned around with the "pepsters" in her sorority, ate "raw eggs" for the heck of it, and asked my dad out to the "gold-digger's ball."

Yes, that woman—what happened to her?

Before she married, my mother seemed carefree and fun loving, but after her wedding, anxiety darkened her days. She found herself trapped in a contest with my father, a gregarious, hard-driving and ambitious optimist who liked to live big and felt more like an adversary than a partner. On April 6, 1961, after fifteen years of marriage, she bought a .44 caliber pistol, drove into a park near our home in Deerfield, Illinois, and killed herself. But even in the second year of her marriage, my mother knew something was terribly wrong. She came to believe that the marriage was in trouble because she and my dad had irreconcilable differences.

Differences that I was born to reconcile.

* * *

From the beginning, the wedding was rocky. At the close of a semester in 1945, my mother was accepted into the nursing program at the University of Kansas Hospital, and sitting among friends at the college canteen, she broke some bad news to my dad. If she entered the program she would only have six weeks of vacation and the first vacation was only a week long. Dad grew sullen. "Six weeks, my God," he grumbled several times as she and their friends tried to change the subject. He had plans to set up a veterinary practice in Dodge City, his hometown in the western part of the state, and hoped that she would drop out of school and marry him. "Bobbie," he blurted out angrily, "one week wouldn't give us *time* to get married."

Her parents had been applying pressure from the other side when marriage seemed likely, urging my mother to complete college. They had always been protective of their only daughter and suspicious of this smooth talker who was as comfortable in boots as in a suit, liked jazz and cars and dancing and fat steaks, and didn't seem to have established himself in his practice yet. In the end, they were probably glad for any plans that might slow down a wedding.

"I do want to please you," she had written to them, feeling anxious about being left alone to dangle between these two choices. "It is such a hard decision and not a single person can help me."

She also felt alone with the choice at the end of her life. By that time my dad was an executive with a pharmaceutical company located in Chicago and was often gone on long trips. I can see her in the living room twisting the rod on the venetian blinds closed and pouring herself a drink. She lifts an album from a stack and eases the record out of its slip, placing it on the changer while moving the heavy arm in position. It is late at night, after my bedtime, but I hear the whoosh of the needle against vinyl and sneak out of bed to watch her from the top of the stairs as the voice of Peggy Lee singing "Fever" fills the lonely room. That was the setting of her final decision and she was alone.

But the earlier choice of marrying my dad was not entirely hers to make. It only seemed that way. "Everything inside of me tells me this isn't the thing to do," Dad said in the canteen after his anger had subsided, referring to the delayed wedding plans. "There is only one thing in the world I want," he added shrewdly, speaking directly to her at this table of friends, "and that is to be married to you—and if this is the only way it can be accomplished—there isn't much I can say." If my mother got the language right here, it comes across as a small speech, spoken in the presence of others, sounding a high note about marriage in the context of a grudging concession, but my father was only temporarily stymied. He may not have had much to say at the time, but he would have the last word.

The next semester my mother moved into the dormitory at the University of Kansas Hospital and signed up for her classes: Pharmacology, Surgical Nursing, Medical Nursing, Professional Adjustment, Nursing Arts II, and Diet Therapy. "Sounds like we'll be busy, doesn't it," she wrote warily. She quickly made friends with the twelve other students in the program: "It is practically like living in a sorority except the girls are a lot friendlier." The bonding became stronger as they studied late into the night for tests and did rounds on the cancer ward together. The patients, who were mainly older women and "pretty grouchy," were very difficult. "They act like we're machines to do their any whim no matter how busy we are," she complained. The new nurses finished each shift exhausted: "Every one of us new students flops on the bed the minute we get back to our rooms after we've been on duty."

She found that, despite the hardships, nursing was rewarding: "I'm so glad I came into training." She called it a "self-satisfying profession" and said that she "always looked forward to going on the floor." She surprised herself with the reservoir of kindness that she and the other nurses drew on to do their work. "It's amazing how sweet and patient you can be." Procedures, such as a "sitz bath" or the "ortho prep" done before surgery may have sounded daunting in class but they were actually simple in practice, and sometimes it was exciting to be part of such important work. "Guess what I just got through seeing," she wrote after observing a delivery: "A Caesarian." Even the depressing duty of working with terminal patients did not get her down: "The patients on 4b (the floor we are on) are mostly late cancer patients. The prognosis of my patient is unfavorable. She has cancer of the uterus and they have given her two transfusions this week." Working amid so much hopelessness was sad, but it did not discourage her. "If this is the worst, I think I'll be very happy because I really do enjoy my work on 4b."

She changed beds, straightened up rooms, bathed patients, filled out charts, and gave enemas, all while wearing heels that made her feet "awfully tired," but in the end she agreed with one of her fellow nurses in training who said, "There is no reason why I should like it, but I do."

Dad fought back by proposing to my mother in December before she entered nurses' training. The ring was beautiful, if modest. "Of course, it isn't large, but it has a gorgeous setting," and she immediately "had to dash back into the house to show all the girls." The night that she said yes, my mother was happy. After dinner my newly engaged parents danced to Gene Krupa's band. "I wasn't really expecting to like his band," Mother wrote, but when she heard Krupa play a few solos and then allow others in the band to take solos as well, she appreciated his modesty and generosity of spirit and, catching glimpses of her ring as she danced, left "completely sold" on the group—and on Dad.

After the proposal my mother set her mind to defending her marriage plans against the objections of my grandparents, who wanted her to go to nursing school and knew that a marriage would jeopardize that ambition. My grandmother also believed that my dad was a "gold digger," marrying a doctor's daughter for the money. My mother defended her future husband and assured her mother that she had not been putting on airs. "Only time will tell if Max thinks he is marrying me for my money," she wrote in an uncharacteristically incoherent sentence, adding defensively that she had not acted in a way that would lead him to think she was wealthy. "Good heavens, I don't have a fur coat, radio, or anything that would give that impression."

In the end, my mother won this battle, which meant that my dad won as well. Not being married simply put too much strain on the relationship. Since Dad had just started his practice in Dodge City, which was three hundred miles from Lawrence, he always arrived late on Saturday, giving him and my mother little time together before her curfew. If they were married she would be able to get an apartment and see him for longer hours on his weekend visits. She also promised that she would finish school. She had made up her mind: "There comes a time when you're ready to be married. If you pass up that time your wedding becomes an anti-climax and a big disappointment."

The wedding was small, limited to family, and many on my dad's side were not able to attend, but my mother called it "just perfect." The service was held in the Methodist church in Glen Elder with a reception outdoors in my grandparents' yard. In the wedding cake photo, my mother wears a white gown and veil with long white gloves and Dad has on a light-toned, double-breasted suit with a carnation boutonniere. The white tablecloth, the cake, and my mother's gown glow in the photograph, shedding light in a nimbus against the dark cottonwoods behind her.

They honeymooned at The Elms, a grand limestone hotel in Excelsior Springs near Kansas City known for its mineral waters, large grounds, and horseback riding. The corner room with large windows was, like the wedding, "just perfect":

"The windows had white Venetian blinds and gorgeous light green drapes. The bedroom suite was of very light wood—with a gorgeous green bed spread." Later in the letter my mother apologizes for using the word *gorgeous* too often, lamenting that her vocabulary was not equal to the grandeur of the hotel, but she certainly conveys her joy and excitement at being there and being married at last.

"We went riding for an hour. The road curved around the green, tree-covered hills that reminded me of the mountains in the East. We came to a white gate. A man was there so he opened it for us and we rode up the lane between two rows of trees." At dinner they had their first taste of champagne. "When the waiter brought us the drink he made quite a procedure out of pouring it into the glass." She drew a small picture of the champagne glass and wrote that the flutes were "very different" and "delicate" with a "stem that is hollow so the champagne flows clear to the bottom." She admitted to some disappointment with the bland taste, but she was captivated by the drink anyway. "Champagne is so beautiful to look at. The bubbles keep rising to the top of the glass and form a miniature fountain."

Two weeks later, she decided to quit the nursing program and join Dad in Dodge City.

By July of 1946, my mother was finished with school and had set up house in Dodge City. The house had air-conditioning, a rarity then, but summer temperatures often rose above a hundred degrees Fahrenheit: "I'm getting to be like a potted plant," she groused, "when I go outside in the afternoon I practically wilt." She had little experience as a housekeeper despite her nurse's training. Dad taught her how to cook by showing her the way to make each dish the first time, and he helped choose the groceries at Peterson's Market in town. Mother also had to clean house, apparently for the first time. "I'm enjoying cooking and keeping house at present," she admitted, but added a telling reservation. "It won't be so much fun when the new wears off."

Still, the changes—the new marriage, a new town, and a house—brought excitement, and the new car, a cream-colored Nash Ambassador, thrilled her. They did not get to choose the color and were pleased when it arrived that it was not a "dirty green" shade. It had a "good-toned radio" and my mother was eager to take her parents for a ride in it when they visited. The most delightful and daunting surprise for her was the gift of Cricket, a black mare. "Last night we went out to see my horse," she wrote. "She certainly is a beautiful thing." Cricket was large— between sixteen and seventeen hands high—with a strong neck and shoulder and a deeply defined jugular groove. "She is coal black—not a white spot on her," and "shines like a million dollars." Every night that they did not have company, my mother and Dad had to drive to the stables and brush her to keep the glossy shine.

My mother was excited about the horse, but anxious as well. "I'm afraid she will throw me because I don't know how to ride." Dad had grown up in Dodge City, a western Kansas town where horses were common, but my mother, from Glen Elder to the east, had little experience with them. So she started slowly, sitting on Cricket while Dad led the mare around a pen. "She isn't completely broken, but she is awfully gentle." Within a month, my mother was riding every night and, in one picture taken by a family friend, she and Dad are both on horseback, my dad in an open-necked dress shirt and my mother wearing pleated riding pants, a short-sleeved white blouse, and gloves. Behind them, the bright Kansas sky is darkening and shadows under the horse barn have begun to lengthen.

It is hard to pinpoint where, exactly, the marriage began to sour, but during the first year in Dodge City my father's world began to eclipse my mother's as she accommodated herself to her role as the wife of a rural veterinarian, and that shift took a toll. Dad's routine was to be up at five and he often did not finish at the animal hospital until nine or ten at night. It was a grueling schedule. During their first year, they used their home as the animal hospital, which provided its own set of challenges, in particular the annoying and incessant barking. "We have ten dogs downstairs," my mother complained, "and would probably have about five more if we only had room for them." Later, when they moved into an apartment separate from the hospital my mother was relieved. It was more "homey" than living above the hospital, and was located in town so that she could walk to the grocery. Above all, she and Dad got away from the noise: "It is wonderful not to hear the dogs barking all of the time. I told Max that I would have been thrilled to live in a tent if necessary to get away from those dogs."

Mom helped Dad at first by keeping the books, and found that she liked the work. Her nurse's training came in handy as she administered shots, gave medications to the cats and dogs, changed bandages, and removed stitches. "Max says it really helps him a lot and I love doing it. Guess I'm just a nurse at heart." In the end, she seemed to thrive on the hard work and lively atmosphere of the hospital. "We haven't done a thing all week but work—but you can't get around it," she mentioned while describing the routine of their twelve-to-fourteen-hour days.

Despite its intensity, though, work seemed more like a distraction from a growing emptiness than a real source of happiness and contentment. My mother often mentions how much she missed school and nurses' training. When she sent a gift to a cousin who entered the nursing program at the university hospital, she got sentimental about school. "I still get a lump in my throat everytime I write to the kids in training." Away from school, she worried about the lack of intellectual challenges. "Yes it is wonderful not having to study all the time, but I'm getting so lazy. I just have to push myself." Above all, she missed home. While Dad was beginning to make contacts that would eventually take him away from the veterinary practice and Kansas, my mother was looking back. "As usual I'm pretty lonesome," she wrote after a visit to her family in Glen Elder.

On the envelope of one of the letters from 1947, Dad made a line drawing of my mother. He was fond of drawing likenesses and this is clearly one of her. She looks young and pretty in the drawing, her hair pulled back from her face, exposing a pearl earring. The mouth appears soft and relaxed, but the jawline is firm and the eyes open wide with anxiety. In May of 1947, when Dodge City was preparing for a "big anniversary celebration" in which the town paid tribute to its colorful past, she could only think of home. "Someway I can't get very excited," she complained. "Guess I'm getting in a rut."

She had been married one year.

After her first year of marriage, my mother was often gloomy and subject to mood swings. She worried about money and believed that my father was not telling her the truth about their finances. Cleaning house became the drudgery she had feared, and she often let it go, feeling guilty. In several letters she mentions the need to push past her doldrums and be more efficient in her housework, but staying upbeat was a struggle. During a week when she laid down new linoleum floors in her kitchen, she lost five pounds and found herself constantly tired, and, in the end, the whole project was nerve-racking. And always, after she visited her parents or they visited her, she wrote about being "lonesome."

In May of 1947, she had to put a tracer on a package that she sent to her mother. At the post office she described the package and its contents and filled out forms with addresses and other information—"a lot of red tape like that." The next day, while cleaning her car, she found the package under boxes of medical supplies in the trunk. Dad had forgotten to send it. "Boy, right then and there I hit the ceiling," she wrote. "I just don't think there is any excuse at all for a man twenty-three years old forgetting to mail a package." It upset her because my dad knew that the package was important to her and still he forgot to send it. The night did not go well. "Anyway, it ended up that I slept in the front room bed and he slept in the bed on the back porch."

In the middle of March in 1948, she went through a particularly bad time. "I was so lazy and slow," she complained, "that it took me all week to get my work done." The snows had been heavy that year—"we certainly are having a winter"—and it had started snowing again, "and hard, too," while she was writing the letter. She had stopped working with my dad at the hospital. "It gets me all upset, and makes me cranky and it isn't worth it." So instead of going to the hospital as she had in the past, she kept the books at the house, and the job that had brought her satisfaction before was now a source of tension. "Max says I'm not worth having around at the hospital," she admitted, a sentiment that must have hurt.

In March, they went rattlesnake hunting on the ranch of their new friends, Buck and Wynona Adams. My mother liked the couple a great deal. Buck was wealthy—"but you would never know it," she wrote, and Wynona "is just as interesting and fun as she can be," but the snake hunt merely reinforced how much different my father and mother were. The Adamses had two viper pits and my mother went with them and my dad to check for snakes. "I was so scared I didn't know what to do," she explained. Fortunately the pits were empty, but the party did not want to go back empty-handed so they started shooting prairie dogs for entertainment, much to my mother's dismay. "I hate to shoot any kind of animal or bird," she wrote, though she admitted that the wildlife was not in danger from her. "I couldn't hit any of them anyway."

By their second anniversary in May of 1948 the differences between my mother and father, which had been there from the beginning, were becoming unbearable. They celebrated with friends on a weekend fishing trip to Lake Meade, about an hour and a half southwest of Dodge City, Kansas, where my dad had set up his veterinary practice. They arrived at the Meade Auto Park and Camping Grounds around eight thirty on Friday and were joined by several married couples, including their new friends Bill and Sue Zimmerman, as well as two single friends, Donnie and Ramona, who were being set up. "Who knows," my mother wrote, "maybe we started a romance."

The presence of Bill and Sue means that the trip was not all pleasure. My parents and Bill Zimmerman had met four months earlier, on a snowy weekend at the Hotel Kansan in Topeka. Bill took them out to dinner and a show as part of a campaign to convince my father to sell his veterinary practice in Dodge City and work for Lederle Labs, a subsidiary of the American Cyanamid Company in New York. The trip to the lake was probably a way to reciprocate, and the night before the drive to the camping grounds, my parents hosted the Zimmermans in Dodge City and "sat up and talked until two." My mother does not say what they talked about, but since Bill was actively recruiting my dad and Sue was probably there to address my mother's concerns and answer her questions, the conversation no doubt turned to the possibility of my father's future with Cyanamid, an initiative which bore fruit two years later. Talking to Bill and Sue gave my mother a glimpse of her future.

At Lake Meade, everyone stayed at the cabins near the cool artesian lake in a Kansan oasis of whispering cottonwoods. The first night the men fished late without catching anything, and my mother had to fry enough chicken to feed everyone while Sue watched. Sue "is very definitely not the domestic type," my mother wrote, but while my mother dipped the chicken breasts in seasoned flour and eased the pieces into the sizzling fat, Sue kept her company in the large kitchen. About my mother's height, but a little thinner, Sue was a blue-eyed blond. Like my mother she had married a gregarious and talkative man and was, herself, quiet and soft-spoken, but in some ways she represented all that my mother had given up when she left college to marry Dad. "She has a good job and she said she would rather work all her life than do the housework." Sue was "pretty quiet," my mother observed, and the two of them may have felt a little awkward in this recruiting situation. Still, despite the contrast—which probably caused anxiety both ways—my mother felt a sympathy with Sue, who clearly fought off some of the same demons that had haunted her since her marriage to Dad. She is "very intelligent and nice to be with," my mother explained, and in her reserved way she offered a relief from Bill. She was "exactly the opposite" of her talkative husband.

"I have just pretty well decided that opposites always marry," my mother realized as she arranged the chicken in the skillet and talked with her blond doppelgänger, a rationalization, to be sure, but one that crystallized the problem in her marriage for the first time.

In a month, she and Dad would be in counseling.

*   *   *

On Friday, June 18, 1948, my parents looked down the long road of their marriage and, terrified by what they saw, sought help. In the two years since they had gotten married, my mother had grown increasingly anxious and depressed and finally confronted Dad. She put it this way in a frank letter home: "Mother, as you know and Daddy probably you know, too, Max and I haven't been getting along too well. Well, last Wednesday evening I gave Max quite a rude awakening to the situation." It is not hard to see what led up to this confrontation: his demanding and exhausting job, his tendency to lie and smooth over difficulties, her gloominess, her sense of failure since she had quit nurses' training and her regrets about that, her nostalgia for home coupled with the sense that she did not really feel at home in Dodge, and, above all, her sense that she and my dad were so different.

So the next day, on Thursday, he found Dr. Jackman and set up the appointment. In the '40s marriage counseling was in its early stages. "He is an M.D.," my mother wrote, "but he uses a lot of psychology along with it." Dr. Jackman was a quiet and sensitive physician—"a little effeminate," as my mother put it, which meant that my dad was probably on guard. Still, the doctor refused to take sides in their argument and seemed to care about each of them. "He is very interested in helping young people with their marriage difficulties." He was a "good listener" who spoke with a calm authority that both my mother and my dad trusted: "Once he starts talking quietly and sincerely, you can't help but listen."

He spoke with each of them alone before seeing them together. When he was finished, he gave a frank appraisal of what he had heard. After listing the strengths in the marriage, he told both of them "frankly and in front of each other" that their "adjustment to marriage" was a "complete failure." He admonished Dad about lying, which did not protect my mother and only hid problems and undermined trust. He prescribed medicine for my mother's chronic sadness and suggested that she return to work at my dad's animal hospital so that she could "be near" her husband and "really become acquainted with him." He also insisted that they immediately take a week's vacation away from home and the pressures of my dad's work. "You must have a few days alone and together." When my parents explained that a vacation at that time was "impossible because of finances," Dr. Jackman remained adamant: "Sell something because your marriage is at stake."

Implicit in Dr. Jackman's recommendations, I think, is the idea that my parents had become sexually distant from each other. His suggestions that they "be near" each other and become "acquainted again" and that they find "a few days alone together" sound like a prescription for a couple that has found sexual intimacy to be a problem, and his final recommendation addressed the matter bluntly. "He also said he thought we should start our family," my mother explained. When she and Dad told him that they both wanted children but felt they had to "postpone them because of finances," Dr. Jackman, who knew how hard it would be for the parallel edges of their lives to meet, rejected the excuse again. Clearly he thought that my mother's anxiety about "finances" was primarily a way to avoid facing the real problems of their marriage: "He said if we would work together instead of against each other our finances would improve."

The therapy session seemed to help. Dad tried, with occasional slips, to walk the hard plank of telling the truth, though the old habit of obfuscation was hard to break: "Max is telling me all about the finances and making himself always tell me the truth. He stumbles once in a while but immediately corrects himself—he is trying very, very hard and I am too." My mother attempted to shed her dark thoughts about their life together. "Max and I are happy for the first time since our marriage," she announced triumphantly, and said that her friends could already tell a difference in her. She writes, cryptically, that the "marriage relationship has already been corrected," probably a veiled way of indicating to her mother that she and my dad were having sex again. She ends the letter with a PS: "I love my husband very, very much and he also feels the same way. *Oh! It is a happy day.*"

These declarations of happiness, which fill the last two pages of the letter, sound brittle. They describe a fragile joy, an exhilaration too easily earned, and the thought that my parents had been unhappy since they had gotten married indicates the depth of the underlying sadness. Still, they took the trip—for two days instead of a week—to Manitou Springs and Pikes Peak, and my mother felt confident enough to make this announcement. "I have so much faith in our marriage and in Max now that we are trying to have a baby."

My birth may have distracted them from their problems for a while. "We're having a wonderful two-day vacation," my mother wrote on a postcard from Pikes Peak in Colorado. Following Dr. Jackman's recommendation, they had gotten away from Dodge, at least briefly. The card is a colorized view of the mountains showing the parallel lines of a switchback road leading up to a snow-covered mountain and meeting at the top. White cumulus clouds glow in an azure sky with a hint of a yellow sunset at the horizon. "We've really kept busy seeing the sights," Mom added. "We're on the Peak now."

By the end of October, my mother thought that she was pregnant. "I'm pretty sure now," she wrote, and planned to see the doctor. "Keep your fingers crossed," she added hopefully. In December my mother had a date: "Baby to be born around June 15. Mother feeling wonderful. Hasn't been sick a day." In January 1949, my mother went shopping in Meade for maternity dresses with her friend Eathel but couldn't find anything to buy. "Eathel was kidding me that I didn't like them because they made me look pregnant," she joked. At her monthly checkup, Dr. Jackman mentioned that she would "be feeling movement anytime now." While pregnant she seemed to have more energy and assured her mother that it was no chore to entertain houseguests. "I sometimes even forget I'm pregnant until I walk in front of a mirror." I arrived early, on June 9, 1949. My grandparents stayed for the month of June, so there are no letters from that time, but by July tenth my mother reported that I was "doing fine" and, when she talked to me, I would smile.

Unfortunately this happy version of my birth as a way to reconcile opposites does not tell the whole story. The truth is far darker, and even the letters which brought joyous news are laced with black threads. "It's so cloudy we can't see a thing," my mother wrote on that postcard from Pikes Peak in Colorado. "Also, lots of snow." Although she and my dad did take Dr. Jackman's advice to get away, they could not afford to spend an entire week, so they made it a long weekend instead, which violated the spirit of the trip, especially since they once again used finances as an excuse. Even with colorization, the scene in the postcard looks desolate, a broken road to nowhere vanishing on a mountaintop that took my mother even farther west from home.

In the third month of her pregnancy, a blizzard struck western Kansas and Dodge City. The newspaper reported eight hundred missing, many of them, including my dad, stranded in cars on the side of the road. He and a friend, Mac McAllister, were on a call near Fowler, a town about thirty-five miles away from home. It was snowing when they left at one o'clock, but no one suspected a blizzard. At 11:15 PM my mother finally called in a report, but she did not learn until 1:15 AM that her husband was safe at a farmhouse. It was clearly a miserable night for the men.

In my mother's letter are clippings from newspapers about hotel lobbies filling with the stranded who spent the night trapped. "As the long-awaited dawn cracked through the ghostly white atmosphere," one paper reported, "tired faces turned gray in its light." The storm disrupted communications and blocked roads throughout southwest Kansas. By the second day there were five known fatalities, including Maxine Laughlin, a thirty-year-old woman from Jetmore who tried to escape the blizzard by car with her seventy-five-year-old mother-in-law. When the car stalled, Maxine attempted to get help on foot, but after trudging a mile or so she collapsed and began crawling. It took the recovery team a day to locate her body, which was "found in a kneeling position" under a five-foot drift of snow, her legs bruised and bloody. She was eight months pregnant.

In the last days of 1948, six months from my birth, my parents' neighbor, Wilson Lane, killed himself in his car, which was parked near the Ford County Lake. He died of carbon monoxide poisoning and police called the death a suicide. My mother learned this news from another neighbor before Dad got home from work, but could not bring herself to visit Lane's wife, Rose, who was her friend. Later Dad went instead and offered to help, and at the funeral he served as a pallbearer. "I've heard so many, many rumors why he committed suicide that I wouldn't know which, if any, were true," my mother wrote anxiously. Outwardly, he had "everything to live for," including a secure job at Combs Automotive Company and three sons. In the letter she speculates on her own mental state and her reluctance to help. "I was nervous and upset," she admitted. Being "nervous" was her euphemism for attacks of anxiety, just as feeling "tired" was code for depression. Both were becoming more of a problem for her. "Usually I'm calm about such things, but since I've been pregnant I tire quicker and get nervous."

After the new year, my mother's friend Margaret had a miscarriage when she fell on the stairs. "She and Stan are practically sick with grief," Mother wrote. "I said they shouldn't feel too bad—surely they'll have another if they could have one." Still my dad cautioned that my mother had better not visit for a few days because Margaret was for the moment inconsolable: "When she sees a pregnant woman," Dad explained, "she bursts into tears."

I arrived on June ninth, and was the center of attention. "People have been dropping in all week to see Steven," Mother wrote, adding that "it has been awfully hard to get my naps in." When I cried, my grandparents calmed me with long rides in their Chrysler, and my grandpa regaled me with faces and antics to get me to smile. It didn't work.

"Steven smiles now," my mother wrote two months after my birth. "Too bad he didn't do that sooner when you folks were here."

It was a failure, of course, this attempt to reconcile differences by having me. The differences which loomed large in 1949 only increased as the family grew and Dad became more successful. But I can say that my parents did try and for that effort, which led to my very existence, I am grateful. It is in my mother's willingness to learn to ride the horse Cricket, though, that I see most clearly her attempt to bridge her differences with my father and save the marriage, an effort she made but could not sustain. "I've been riding Cricket every night," she wrote on August 5, 1946, when her marriage was new. She and Dad could not yet afford a saddle, so she borrowed one from a friend, but she announced proudly that they had just bought a new bridle that morning. Still eager to demonstrate that she was adjusting to her new life, my mother learned to ride and spent time training her horse in order "to show off a little" when her parents visited. "I have ridden Cricket for three nights straight," she explained, and added that she would probably have to continue that regimen for two or three weeks in order for her and her horse to become completely comfortable with each other. "She sure takes a lot of time, but she is worth it."

A month later my mother felt confident enough for an all-day trip with my father. "We rode Cricket and Princess on a ten mile ride along the creek Sunday morning." The terrain would have been irregular prairie land marked by low slopes and fractured, windblown bluffs of silt and sand and sandstone. As they made their way along the stream on horseback, they would have observed a landscape of grasses. In the south, buffalo grass colors the sandy plains with low-lying stretches of apple green and mingles with the purple shades of blue grama, a short grass with dark, eyelash-seed heads. North of town, the short grasses give way to taller mixed grasses of bluestem and side oats, especially along the stream beds, where stretches of light green are suffused with the darkening of the bluish stems. Mixed in with these prairie grasses my parents would have passed fields of winter wheat and milo planted in large sections. From horseback, the largely treeless plains would have appeared as a palette of subtle browns, greens, and blues.

By now my mother, who exercised her horse almost every evening, could ride well, and the all-day adventure suggests how accomplished she had become in a matter of months. "We rested our horses four times, and let them eat grass," my mother wrote. "It was beautiful."

The loneliness of my mother's decision to marry my dad filled her with anxiety. "Not a single person can help me," she complained, struggling with her choice. So it is a measure of the depth of her despair fourteen years later that she was able to make the loneliest decision of all. After dropping my father off at the train station, she found an isolated spot in a nearby park—followed by a suspicious policeman who trailed at a distance—stepped out of her car, and, even though she hated "to shoot any kind of animal or bird," turned the gun on herself and pulled the trigger. By that time, after years of suffering and depression, it may not have been a difficult decision at all, but the inevitable conclusion of a piling on of events. The parallel paths of my parents' lives met at the vanishing point. In my last memory of her, she is alone, looking into the record console late at night with her back to me as she listens to jazz, swaying to the sound of Peggy Lee, drink in hand. The song is "Fever," with the refrain "what a lovely way to burn," and she sings the line over and over, holding the notes out, trying to sound good. By then, I suspect, the choice had been made.

I like to imagine the time before she gave up, when she joined Dad for nightly rides across the prairie land around Dodge City as dusk settled over western Kansas. I picture them—young, newly married, and hopeful—trotting slowly through limestone rubble scattered along riverbanks and wooded ravines. From horseback they could look out on long stretches of ranchland interrupted here and there by windbreaks of ash, elm, cottonwood, and oak. In spring, wildflowers added streaks of blue and purple to the open fields where cattle gathered at wateringholes and deer hid among clumps of blooming barberry, mock orange, and privet. Crests of hills opened onto panoramic vistas of fields, prairie lands, and streams, geese flying overhead in formation, honking while seeking nightly shelter on ponds and creeks. "It's stunning," my mother wrote in letters home, looking out on a broad and desolate horizon, knowing that her words were inadequate. "Gorgeous."

BRIAN SWANN

Imago Mundi

inside the paperweight
        bubbles,
                one poised on the tip
                        of a petal
     from which it can never launch,
            others are galaxies peppered here
& there round the pansy,
             "thought,"
       whose saffron streaks are neat as hand-
     painted, floating like an untethered
astronaut in
     "the artifice of eternity,"
                 while outside
       midwinter snow sits
   like bleakmindedness
      until light rings, vivid as a pin,
       grass spurts
         & the field
   becomes a razzle
     of butterflies, sky
    a field of sunflowers so vivid
   it's
     invisible
        as trout, the color of water,
  a flash where water's glass
             bending
     the world
as tonight,
   where the sky flowers
       & stars give off scents,

drop bright fruit fish rise to,
     taking in constellations,
   & the moon turns
  over flips
in the lake's shivering mirror, the same in all directions
  so I enter quietly, steering
      stars aside,
   moving weightless as a bubble,
       floating in eternity

JEREDITH MERRIN

The Art of Living

We have more than a room—rooms!—in our little house.

All over America people are getting fat in front of their flat screens, eating junk.

All over our pretty house yesterday grievance plastered the walls.

I'm just sayin'.

Perpetrating misery in (practically) luxury's lap; how evil is that?

It's so last week, so over.

Get up, little darlin'. I'll make you an egg.

New Year

Praise to the man or woman who stays open
to the river of each day. Praise
to her or him who keeps, past sixty
and in all weathers, an open heart.

Remember nineteen? The pair of us walking at midnight
in the city and stopping at someone's, anyone's, front stairs
(those concrete steps, the Richmond in San Francisco)
—ignoring the cold, ignoring the strangers who must
be annoyed inside—to sit and talk excitedly, laughing
or moving ourselves to tears like Chekhov's drunken Russians,
needing to *say* the vast, inrushing perceptions of just one day.

      —You weren't the one I walked with. I let the poem lie,
knowing it wouldn't matter: you'd have your own city,
you'd have been giddy before you grew old, and apprised.

Praise to the man or woman who stays open
to the river of each day. Praise
to her or him who keeps, past sixty
and in all weathers, an open heart.

HENRY HART

The Angry Man

Do you see them—the dead
  mother with her nestlings
cupped in his scaly hands?

One ant creeps over the nest
  to assess the damage—eyes
glued shut, beaks pried open

as if squabbling over a last inchworm.
  My neighbor snaps,
"Your wrens killed my bluebirds."

He sucks in stubbled cheeks,
  hobbles past torches
of forsythia to gas cans in his garage.

A wren flits from branch
  to branch in my crape myrtle,
caterwauls like a diva in a bad opera.

Next morning, smoke leaks
  through bedroom windows.
Charred burlap hangs from nails

on my wren-house post.
  In flip-flops I shuffle
to the hedge that divides our yards,

scoop up burnt wings
      and skulls in a dustpan,
bury them by pepper roots in the garden.

All morning, words flare
      on my screen, black as moons
of dirt beneath my nails.

The sky darkens with wings,
      glistens
with the furious eyes of wrens.

AISHA SABATINI SLOAN

The Strong Man and the Clown

COFFEE SPITS AT ME from a small paper cup as I walk down the gangway in the airport. "Why does coffee spit?" I ask. My dad, who for as long as I can remember has been jotting down quotes in a thin, beige notebook, says, "Coffee spitting, now that's a good opener." "Yeah, and I'm going to use it." My mom laughs. My father feigns disappointment. We are at the end of a layover in Ohio, on our seventh trip to Italy as a family.

During the layover my mom asks me to put some Icy Hot on her back, so we march to the nearest rest room. She waits for me to pee, standing near the sink where she has uncapped the Icy Hot. It looks like a stick of deodorant. A woman who has just washed her hands seems lost and my mom smiles sweetly, pointing to the paper towel dispenser with her trusty stick of Icy Hot. The woman makes it clear that she doesn't know what my mother is doing. My mom puts the Icy Hot on the counter and then says to me, "I'm going to pee; watch this," and I entertain the thought that perhaps this woman thinks my mom is crazy, as I look unrelated to her—a black woman across the bathroom from a small white lady, who is con-stantly motioning to people with deodorant. When she gets back from using the bathroom, she bends her neck forward and I apply the salve.

"You know what I'm looking forward to?" she asks as we walk back to the gate. "Dinners. Are you writing down everything I'm saying?"

I know what she means because I too was there that night in Assisi when we ate pasta with truffles. I remember the way the food tasted, how we had a sense of discovery in our blood, as though we were scouting out new territory to settle for the strange nation we as a family composed. We visited a friend and I ran through her property, picking young, green apples from her trees. She was black, a dancer, and her house was full of hardwood floors, draping fabric, and mirrors. She lived in what felt to be a forest. It was as though we'd made contact with a resident of a little-known, distant moon.

Once we board the plane, it gets dark. We are surrounded, for a moment, by small monitors on seat backs, each one showing a glowing yellow topographical map of Ohio and Kentucky and Indiana. Light glances off my parents' held hands. A cartoon of a plane taking off into a blue-and-white sky plays as our own plane ascends into night.

One of the great tragedies of our early vacations to Italy was the loss of the Pinocchio dolls. My mother fell in love with the smooth red-and-green figures, and several were stolen from our suitcases. So for me, memories of Italy are imbued with the Italian fairy tale. As the story goes, a newly carved Pinocchio leaves home one day, waving sweetly to his father. Neither of them realize how far he must journey before he can come home again.

Pinocchio is the story of a puppet, yes. But it is also the story of a child who turned out differently from what his father had intended.

My mother was disowned by her father around the same time that she started dating my dad. As she tells it, he disowned her because she moved out of the family house to live with friends at a time when Italian girls, even in Detroit, weren't allowed to leave home without a husband. He died not long after this silence settled between them.

The greatest surge of Italians to move to the United States occurred during the period from 1880 until 1920. Four million Italians immigrated during this time. The poor economy after unification sent many young men away to forge a new life for their families. My mother was not the only daughter of this migration who fell in love with a black man.

In *Jungle Fever*, Italian American Angie Tucci gets punched and kicked by her father as punishment for her relationship with a black architect named Flipper Purify. He shouts after her, "I'd rather stab myself in the heart with a knife than be the father of a nigger-lover." The verb *whale* means "to whip, flagellate, flog, hide, larrup, lash, scourge, stripe, thrash, wear out." My mother swears that her father didn't know she was dating a black man. "He would have been upset," she says, "but I think if he knew Daddy he would have come around." He was not a bigot, from anyone's recollection. Any person she brought into the house was to be treated with respect, and my mother's friends came from all kinds of backgrounds. If there wasn't enough food, it went to the guest first. She has little memory of him saying anything negative about other ethnic groups. But it was the sixties. In Detroit. There had been that riot.

This story wants to be one of redemption. Of a man who crawls onto a deserted beach filled with anguish and regret. Some Anthony Quinn, breaking his fist on the sand with sadness over the loss of his daughter. But of course, it falls somewhere short of that. What we know for sure is that in 1922, a twenty-two-year-old with four-inch-tall hair as rugged as a rock cliff gazed out of a porthole in third class on a ship headed for Ellis Island. He wore the tattoo of a naked lady on his arm, which he'd gotten years before when the circus came to town. He may have known that once in America, he would become a boxer. He may have been planning to bury fruit trees in winter, to tie together cut branches coated in zinc in spring to inspire the growth of hybrid fruit. He may have known that he would hunt for dandelions along the edges of his neighbor's property to use for salads and sautés. But surely he had no clue that the family he was about to start would move back across the Mediterranean with Africa in its blood.

The plot of *Pinocchio* is familiar, in part, because it involves a man being swallowed by a whale. The Book of Jonah tells another version of this story. Jonah is trying to run away from a task that God has given him: to warn the wayward people of Nineveh that their town will be destroyed unless they ask for God's forgiveness. It is an action plot, in some ways, a divine car chase. Jonah runs from his duty, and God follows him with tempests and whales. It becomes harder to run when Jonah realizes that other lives are at stake.

When the boat he's boarded gets caught in a storm, Jonah tells a group of mariners, "Take me up, and cast me forth into the sea; so shall the sea be calm unto you: for I know that for my sake this great tempest is upon you." In an illustrated version of the King James Bible, there is a rendering of Jonah in the water. He is an old man, gazing to his right. Behind him like a shadow stands the great tail of a whale. It looks as though he is about to be swallowed. But he looks stubborn, willfully ignoring the presence lurking behind and beneath. This image in particular helps convey the moment I am so fascinated by: my mother and her father suspended, chest deep in some story they've wandered into, not particularly innocent or guilty of much, but not prepared either to forget or forgive. In this snapshot of time, their relationship is forever about to be swallowed into a dream from which it might never wake.

A whale is a mammal. Synonyms for it include *giant, behemoth, leviathan, mammoth, monster.* I was a child of the "Save the Whales" generation. To me, the term connotes a universe of gray, blue, and green. The kind of melancholy you'd find in a Miles Davis song or a museum. When I think of the sea creature who swallowed Jonah, or the whale from *Pinocchio* who swallowed a father and his long lost child, I don't see an angry monster like Monstro. I wonder about the whale's own longings and loneliness. Emotions for which his body becomes a metaphor.

In college, I took a course on Italian neorealism. Scenes from *L'Avventura*, *Roma, Citta Aperta*, *La Terra Trema*, *Umberto D*, and *La Strada* mix with my own memories of Italy: sleepily muttered fairy tales and the particular pronunciation of an Italian man singing, "If you're going to San Francisco, be sure to wear some flowers in your hair" as we sat in La Capriciosa in Rome.

Of all the filmmakers, Michelangelo Antonioni and Federico Fellini captured my imagination the most. During a subsequent trip to Italy in college, I was reading a book of interviews with Fellini. I finished it one afternoon in the room of a pensione, the sound of Rome traffic floating through the red curtains along with pink light. That vacation was spent seeking Fellini-esque visions in every alley, every fountain, every old man's iris.

Many of Fellini's films involve a circus: *The Clowns, La Strada, Juliet of the Spirits*. If not an outright production with clowns, at least some incarnation of touring eccentrics who visit small towns and, in passing, electrify the imagination. A tightrope walker or strong man.

When I think of the first trips we took to central Italy, where my grandfather grew up, I come up against the scene of us walking down a dirt road toward a fair or circus. Flickers of noise and the tungsten glow of an unseen tent strain at my memory, though this part is my invention. When I recently asked my mother about it, she told me that this wasn't a circus, it was a fair put on by the Communist Party. "It was funny," she said. "There was this horrible rock band."

We drove from Balsorano to Il Castello di L'Aquila listening to *The Phantom of the Opera* and picked blackberries along the edges of the castle. I spent hours with a frail woman while opening our way through a set of Russian dolls. My ninth birthday was ushered in by a chorus of Italian widows singing "Ave Maria" as they wove through the small, candlelit dining room carrying an ice cream cake from a nearby bar. My diabetic father ate a spoonful, an unusual sacrifice made in the name of celebration. Nobody was a contortionist or a clown, but the laws defining our reality had definitely shifted. The boundary we'd crossed, manned by security guards with machine guns and German shepherds at the Leonardo da Vinci-Fiumicino Airport was also a spiritual threshold. An answer to our unasked questions: What would have happened if my grandfather hadn't died? What stories live on the other side of forgiveness?

One of my favorite Fellini films, *La Strada*, was filmed, among other places, in L'Aquila. I wonder how far he was from my grandfather's village when in the early 1950s, Fellini had a cord strung up between two buildings to keep a tightrope walker suspended in the air. I imagine the sounds of laughter and awe hitting the valley walls, echoing like dancing light against the steep hills of Rocca Vecchia.

A whale is like a mountain, a presence to which we have become accustomed. There it looms, quiet in the distance. But at any moment, the shape that was a landscape might start to move, water sluicing off the tail. In elementary school, we took a whale watching field trip. I vaguely recall the sound of people's voices as the enormous blue creatures jumped up and flipped over in the ocean. To be in the presence of such large bodies was exhilarating.

In *The Year of the Whale*, Victor B. Scheffer writes, "From the moment of its birth until its final hour, day and night, [the whale] hears the endless orchestra of life around its massive frame. Silence is an unknown thing." The whale hears with its body. "It feels the music, too, for water presses firmly on its frame—a smooth, continuous sounding board."

In the Disney cartoon, Pinocchio's first adventure is to join Stromboli's circus. Something about the garish lights and clumsy, sexualized puppets turns the adventure menacing and surreal. He is a boy confronted for the first time with the hollow pleasures of adulthood, and this mounting shadow of evil becomes the driving tension in the story. As an audience, we are not waiting for him to fall in love or conquer a dragon, we are rooting for him to maintain his innocence. Our reprieve comes in the moments when his innocence is what connects him to other people. On stage, for example, he slips up, gets caught in a mess of string, and makes the audience laugh. This gives him honest joy.

In *La Strada*, Gelsomina is sold to a circus strong man by her extraordinarily poor family. She is an odd little person, with the temperament of a small child and the face, she is told, of an artichoke. During their act, Zampanò and Gelsomina stand facing each other, a shirtless strong man and a painted clown. She surprises herself when she recites her lines and gets the audience to laugh. As it turns out, making people happy is right up her alley.

Zampanò says that sensitive members of the audience might want to look away as he breaks the thick chain wrapped around his body with the muscles in his chest. Gelsomina is the only one in the crowd who seems even remotely ill at ease at the spectacle. When Zampanò accidentally kills the circus fool, Gelsomina repeats the fact to herself with astonishment, stuck in the moment when she rushed to the injured man's side. Her wide-eyed innocence in the face of true pain makes her a natural clown.

Once, while walking to a restaurant on my seventeenth birthday, my family saw an old man get hit by a younger man. When his head hit the cement with an audible thud, my mother wiggled forward in outrage. "No!" she called out. She went dangerously close to the aggressor. "Don't do that to him," she said, as though she could make a case to have the moment removed from time. It seems sometimes that my mother reacts to violence and cruelty as though they are accidents. Aberrations in human nature, rather than the rule.

When my mom went to visit her father before he died, my grandmother told her not to go too close to the bed. "It's best not to upset him," she said. I can't conjure the expression my mother must have worn, hovering in the corner like a naughty child. Her father left the world that night, in the middle of their grudge.

They had always had a stormy relationship. My aunts and uncles shout with laughter about the way my mother got along with their father when she was a teenager. They were like a Tom and Jerry act, Wile E. Coyote and the Road Runner, a pair of stubborn creatures forever engaged in some kind of face-off. When she was young, every night she knocked over her water glass, and her father fumed with irritation. She refused to eat the roasted fowl for dinner on the day their pet ducks disappeared. When she was sixteen, he got angry with her for breaking curfew. "Kill me! Kill me! You're going to have to pay for the funeral!" she screamed, tearing at her shirt. "Did I ever tell you about the time I hid in the shower?" she asks. If he ever did find out that she'd had a child with a black man, I imagine it would be further proof to him that his daughter was, by nature, an entity beyond his comprehension or control.

"What were you like as a little girl?" I ask my mother. "Skinny, curious, sensitive. I would get my feelings hurt easily. I always tried to please people. Shy. Talkative." "What did people say about you?" "I was a little actress. I was very dramatic."

I've noticed, of late, that a lot of comedic actors resemble the star of Fellini's *La Strada*, his beloved wife, Giulietta Masina. In *Happy-Go-Lucky*, for example, Sally Hawkins opens her eyes wide and purses her lips, working with religious zeal to get the people she loves to smile. As a child, I spooned out bowls full of tomato sauce that my mother and grandmother had set to simmering on the stove, then rushed back to the television to watch the way Lucille Ball's eyes blazed, the way she opened her arms into a circle as a way of saying "pizza" in Italian, her vaudevillian tendency to march and masquerade. I only realize now that these expressions remind me of my mother. And while this penchant for drama and exaggeration may simply be a way of eliciting chuckles from the studio audience, in all of these women, there lives a quality of compassion. Theirs is an effort to shift the tone of a chaotic world. If only everyone could be happy, they seem to be saying. What if everything was going to be all right?

Walking down the street of her father's village one afternoon, my mother taps me on the shoulder with animation. "That's how my father would walk!" she says, pointing to her cousin, Duilio. She hurries forward to walk alongside the man, gathering her hands behind her back and swaying her hips like Charlie Chaplin. She turns her head to wink at me before continuing along. In her comedic disposition lives impossible hope: a mime's attempt at reckoning with the ghost.

"Where is my home?" Gelsomina asks Zampanò. They are on the beach, miles from her own seaside town. "Over there," he says, gesturing vaguely off into the distance. There is always, between them, a silent pressure, an invisible wrestling match between their different types of strength, between their quiet, carried burdens.

One year on Christmas, I received two novels by Thomas Wolfe, *Look Homeward, Angel* and *You Can't Go Home Again*. Knowing my parents, these books were chosen less for their contents and more for their names. On the title page of the latter, my mother wrote, "You can always come home." This is not particularly surprising. My mother loves me with the blind loyalty of those Italian mothers you see in the movies. I don't think these characters are exaggerated. What I hear in this inscription about returning home is the converse truth she had to live with: at the mercy of all that silence, all those pent-up explanations, she could not go back.

At a certain point, the rest of the community began to know that my mom was dating my father. "How dare you shop so close to your mother's house," a family friend hissed when she saw my mother out for groceries one afternoon. Whether or not my grandfather knew about my father before he died will always remain a question.

Not too long after my parents started dating, my father got a job in Los Angeles. My mother had no idea what to do with her future. She'd lost interest in becoming an occupational therapist because the year she started, the program instituted a requirement that students dissect a cadaver. She had broken up with a sailor who went off to join the Navy. A friend had invited her to live on the island of Saint Thomas. "You could have been a redhead," she tells me. And I try to imagine feeling like myself as a white child, or whatever I would have been, running along the beaches of the Caribbean.

Poised at the brink of decision, my twenty-two-year-old mother went with her own mother to Quebec for the World's Fair. This is the same fair where, in the late nineteenth century, Africans were displayed, and where the Eiffel Tower was first unveiled. The shifting blueprint for a great unknown stood before her as she traversed the streets of the foreign city in winter. Joining my father in Los Angeles would mean building a future for herself, inventing a life entirely from scratch. "Everything was underground," she says, still astonished at the thought of Montreal's winter architecture forty years later.

Of all her father's children, my mother's journey—her questions, her risk taking—most resembles his own, despite the fact that they seemed completely incapable of understanding one another. She remembers car rides when the two of them, en route to the airport to visit her sister or to a geology field trip, had nothing to say to one another. But they both ended up farther than any of their siblings from the house where they grew up.

Six months after I sat in a beat-up white Nissan in a Detroit U-Haul parking lot with my cousin Travis, looking at *Artforum* magazine and wondering with him, "How do people go to *biennales*?" I find myself in Venice, accidentally in time to see the 2011 biennale myself. The first artist I notice when I stroll in is a black American named Rashid Johnson, whose installation includes mirrored bookshelves and multiple copies of Bill Cosby's *Fatherhood*. The living room evoked here, in a Venetian arsenal, resembles my own: the Cosby books, the coffee table made of mirrors.

There is a video where girls drag their hands along the sand of the beach. There is a video where a blind Dominican man carries a legless Haitian woman around city streets. There is a wax rendition of a famous sculpture melting. There is a simulacrum of a living room where a collage of projected scenes from a movie acts as a clock. There is a room full of giant, dreamlike stone figures that have been made by an artist for his dead child. A video installation mimics an elevator, provoking a sense of movement and vertigo.

At the elbow of one segment of the show, I walk out into a temporary café. The sky is dark with inky clouds despite the fact that a white-hot sun beats down from the other direction. It has just rained. Everyone sits on chairs that remind me of white Play-Doh, amid bubble-shaped lamps, under a giant iron pulley. We are on the water; there is a gondola bobbing idly in the Pirates of the Caribbean–colored lagoon. People are drinking wine in plastic cups or espresso in paper cups. A woman with white hair eats ice cream. We are starting to look at each other like art. A sculpture of a giant whale lies in the sand nearby. It is as if we have all entered into the same dream. I can hear the strains of Nino Rota, the delighted chords of whimsy as a woman dreams up a scene while dozing on the beach in a Fellini film: a cluster of children rolling giant wheels, men in white, fragments from the subconscious parading onto the shore, arriving from or embarking upon the body of the ocean.

In Fellini's *Juliet of the Spirits*, Giulietta Masina's character dreams that a man in a red robe is whispering to her. He asks her to help him drag a rope from the ocean. She looks up to see a boat full of people with strange markings. A black man with a beard stands in profile, holding a sword, and he looks back at the beach toward her. In another dream, a door opens to a room full of people frozen in time. There is a black man, dreadlocked hair held by sticks in what looks to be a Japanese bun, a white woman with white face paint, a short white man in his underwear with his mouth open, women in veils. I wonder how blackness lived inside my grandfather's subconscious. If one kind of blackness ever held the place of another.

It occurs to me that the World's Fair and to an extent, the Venice Biennale are visions of the future, attempts to explain the journey out of our current set of troubles and conflicts. There is an enormous amount of reference to war and violence. Each piece is its own version of a map that could guide us from the country of one mind to the country of another.

In order to get the airport shuttle, I ride a vaporetto from the Palanca stop to Piazzale Roma just before four o'clock in the morning. I almost miss the 3:48 AM departure, and sit breathing heavily, my backpack taking up most of the seat behind me, its straps bracing my shoulders like two strong hands. Listening to *Sketches of Spain* for the duration of the ride through the dark makes me feel sure that Miles Davis composed the album in the middle of the night. As we swing around the curves of the Venetian lagoon, I feel as though I am hearing the music for the first time. The confluence of his music with the way the boat moves slowly in that silence gives me a new sense of rootedness in Italy. Jazz seems at times like a form of citizenship: the black man's passport to Europe. As we edge up against the adagio, moving exactly along the logic of its liquid phrasing, I stake new claim to the country of my grandfather's birth.

In Hal Whitehead's *Voyage to the Whales*, he writes, "Many have tried to describe the song of the humpback, but it is more than 'sonorous groans' or 'unearthly wails.' They use the highest notes we can hear, and all in between, to construct an elegant adagio."

As I watch *Pinocchio* again, I am struck by how old Geppetto is. He is a white-haired man in a house full of clocks, surrounded by the sound of ticking. When he carves from wood the son he never had, his loneliness is transformed from a vacancy to a solid form. Later on, trapped inside the belly of the whale, he floats in a universe as expansive as the sky: a place where time expands and contracts, where light is not always a reflection of the sun. Here, his solitude magnified, we can see the way his life must have felt on land. This story might not be about the boy at all, but rather about the sad fantasies of a man who, toward the end of his life, has come to question the notion of home if the house is empty.

On our seventh trip to Italy as a family, we traveled from Rome by ship. When we boarded, we came to find that the ship was named *Freedom*, so my mother sang protest songs and clapped. Some days I would go to the ship's gym and lie in the sauna to warm up, as I was constantly cold. I had a porthole all to myself, where I could confront the enormity of the ocean alone. This was a preoccupation of mine. It would be a shame, after all, to go to sea without admitting to the scope of it. It was hard to find these moments where I could let the illusion of solidity offered by all-day buffets and talk of postcards dissolve like a haze and stare at the horizon, sense the fathoms below.

In elementary school, we spent quite a bit of time studying whales. For weeks we listened to recordings of whales calling after each other, watched the fictional scientists in *The Voyage of the Mimi* desalinate seawater while stranded on an island, where they studied the ways whales migrated and fed. More than species names or behavioral patterns, a more subtle lesson stays with me from that curriculum: the ocean is a lonely drift, yes, but it is also a place where sound travels faster than in air. The voice of a whale takes less time to reach a calf. Beneath our ship, I imagined that the vibrations of whale song spread out like sleep between bodies, a moaned note with the same texture as love or heat. One night our ship shook as violently as an airplane flying through a storm.

One of the excursions for the cruise was to Pompeii. Our tour guide, with an uncanny resemblance to the actor Roberto Benigni, had a kind of fantastic boredom about him. This was evident in his rumpled attire, and in his tired recitation of facts. But he also wore pink, and had a wry smile, which insinuated that perhaps it was not the world that bored him, but the way in which he had to present it to a bus full of tourists who take in entire cities—the city of his birth—in a few hours, from behind panels of glass. He amused me—and also, he kept looking at me. Not with a leer, but with the kind of recognition you might not know the foundations of, but you'd just as soon accept. If you feel kindred, then hey, so do I.

My father and I asked the tour guide to hold the bus for a moment while my mother used the bathroom, and we stood chatting with him in the sun as the bus of tourists idled. "What did you do before this?" my father asked. "I a-was a teacher." "What age?" "Teenagers." The cell phones and the flirting and the ignoring just about ruined his soul. But he had to make a living, so he got involved with the tourist trade. "What did you do before that?" my father asked. "I went-a to school." "What did you study?" I chimed in. "Jean Cocteau. A French writer." This was perhaps the most interesting fact I'd heard all day. "I just saw one of his films back home," I said. "Yes," our guide smiled. "He made films as well." I could have sworn he felt proud of me in that moment, as though I were the only student in his class of tourists who'd been paying attention.

Back on the bus I replay scenes from *Testament of Orpheus* in my head as we mount a hill, verging closer to Pompeii. Cocteau's black-and-white reel of images plays against the color of the world outside: backward flowing water and disappearing angels superimposed against the blue ocean, small European cars, and tall buildings. The magic of Cocteau hums for the driver, perhaps, beneath the humdrum of this silly institution, this cheap but lucrative stand-in for true curiosity.

After wandering through the ruins, staring into the empty baths, trying to put life back into the petrified bodies killed by Mount Vesuvius and preserved by her cooled lava, after studying the walls of the ancient brothel with its "instructive" tableau, we prepare to reboard the bus. We are early this time, and chat again with our driver. "You are a-lucky to have two women," he tells my father. "And you? Do you have two women in your life?" my mom asks. "Since one month. My daughter is just born." He turns to me, without wryness or mystery, and gazes straight into my eyes. "She looks a-like you. This is why I am so often looking at you. My wife, she is from Colombia." He turns to my father and points to him. "She has a-skin like yours." They named their daughter after a John Coltrane song.

Cocteau says that beauty is always the result of an accident. Somewhere inside me, the fist of fear that I've always held, clasped in the notion that my grandfather wouldn't have wanted to know me, begins to loosen. Our family's strange little unit has been tucked and rooted more firmly in the soil of something irrefutably Italian—amid bodies more ancient, even, than the one in my grandfather's grave.

A homeless Senegalese painter named Joseph once told me something odd. We were standing in Paris, in the cave of his temporary studio—a nook between buildings tucked away from traffic where his paintings were leaned and stacked. I wanted to buy something from him, but he refused to speak to me straight. He was drunk, and spoke in mystic fragments. He said, "Before he died, your grandfather cried my name."

Both of my grandfathers had reason enough to do this. My paternal grandfather was named Joseph, and my mother's father had a Joseph for an eldest son. This moment gave me reason to consider the scene of both grandfathers on their deathbeds. What could have been said in the absence of a listener? On his deathbed, Fellini cried for Giulietta.

A whale is a lurking presence. An indication of the depth that the surface of a story cannot afford to utter. And yet there is the notion of these underwater moans. The way the truth blooms somewhere, in a last breath or underwater. Victor B. Scheffer imagines the sonic history of a whale: "Today he hears another sound like an interstellar cry. It starts as an eerie moan without dimension, formless, leaving the little calf frozen. From whence the cry? It never comes again. Perhaps a creature from the deep as yet unknown to man? Perhaps an ordinary animal, far beyond its normal haunts? Perhaps a silent creature forced to break its silence by some agonizing pain?" I've had occasion to wonder whether emotions, the ones that come on strong and strange with little provocation, are rippling out from the past or latitudinally, the fog of shame or longing or laughter floating around the atmosphere, catching in us briefly like ancestral whispering.

Once upon a time, my grandmother, father, mother, and I got off a train in a small Italian town. We visited the small room, a cellar really, where my grandfather had lived with all his siblings. Our cousins fed us strawberry wine. Olive trees waved in the wind like green ash. "My father had hands as hard as rocks," my mother remembers, "from all that work." So did Minicucci, his best friend from

133

childhood, whom we went to see during the course of our visit. Scientists cannot calculate how long it takes for a father's wish for redemption to travel across the threshold of death to reach the waiting heart of his child. But when the rock-hard hands of a short, surrogate Italian slammed up against my father's head, it was for the purpose of drawing him closer. He gave my father a kiss on each cheek and welcomed him inside.

IDRIS ANDERSON

Sawdust Mountain

My father loaned money to my uncles
for a logging business. They never paid him back.
When I was little it wasn't much I understood
about the loan but we'd visit the mill sometimes
where big trees were brought in on trucks,
longleaf pines trimmed up, branches stripped off.
They used chains and tractors to haul them up
on the logger with its mechanism of pulleys and hooks,
the clank and screech of rusty gears, then the high
wheeling swing of a log. In the blue diesel mist
and cough, I saw the biggest round cutting blade
with teeth like a dragon's teeth. It's what I thought of
when my teacher told us a story about a dragon.

We were studying medieval times and magical beasts
like unicorns and dragons, sea monsters on old maps,
the legend of Tristan with a nick in his sword
for the dragon he killed for his uncle Mark.
I wasn't so sure about uncles and so I had a clue
about how the story would end, pledges and lies,
a black not a white sail on the horizon.

The best part about going to the sawmill
was the sawdust pile. There was one big mountain
of sawdust way on the back of the lumberyard,
a mountain with high multiple peaks, rust orange,
dark brown in places, and black rotten inside.
You know wood can rot, my father said,
and told me the true story of a child climbing

an old sawdust pile. It caved in and smothered her.
But he let me and my sister play on the new pile,
sweet sawdust of pine, not like dust you'd have
on your furniture, but bits and curls of wood
where the saw blade chewed longways down the logs.
We shook it from our hair and socks and pockets.
Sawdust is lighter than beach sand which is gritty
and packs down. You can't make sand castles
with sawdust but you can slide or roll down
from a sawdust mountain and tumble softly to the bottom.

In the mill office my dad and my uncles talked,
joked around, and smoked cigarettes. You could hear
my dad's laugh for a mile. He was a good storyteller.
He'd come out with a handshake and a check in his pocket—
only for interest, I heard them say; they'd pay down
the principal when debts for equipment were clear.
Sometimes the check was good, sometimes bad.
I got bits and pieces of the story, how my dad
wanted to help my uncles, because he could,
with money he'd saved when he was in the war.
They were my mother's brothers. Family, he'd say.
That's when I learned about family and money.

They were taking in big money on the accounts
and bought fancy cars—a white Buick,
a red Thunderbird. Then a timber company
from out of state moved in on them and bought up
tracts of land for the trees. They clear-cut
to raw stumps, then sold it off to developers.
My uncles were smart and put their houses in the names
of their wives, and lost everything else. Everything.

Those were hard times for my father. He ruminated
about it, sipping his coffee, making grocery lists

from the specials in the Thursday paper. He ruminated
about what went wrong, the premature elation of cash
in their pockets, the good times, the big cars.

He liked to watch his daughters sliding, tumbling
down the mountain of sawdust, the simple soft
pleasure of yielding to gravity, while gravity
was a physical thing, not a worry about the way
things were working out in the world. He'd tell us
how growing up as a boy he'd found an orange
in the toe of a sock laid on the hearth of a Christmas fire—
an exotic thing, a bright bitter sweetness.

I learned that hope is a kind of denial, white lies
you tell to yourself to be the kind of person
you can look in the mirror at, lies you wouldn't
believe unless you yourself were good
and hopeful enough to believe in the word of a man.

ANGIE MACRI

Vixit, Chaoniae

Old Lorimer Cemetery

The river swells and bears, then thins
some summers so that you might
step across it. Her father's mill grinds
wheat to flour, screw turning in its current.
Lewis notes her as *agreeable, affable,*
at the age of puberty, the most beautiful
female since Kentucky. Flour
slides downriver like silt.

Her father, commandant of the Spanish
land grant, trades with Kaskaskia
and Sainte Genevieve. Her mother
with much circumspection performed the honours
of the table. Voices widen over the river
from the Red House, spaced as rain on a goblet's side.

Osage orange holds its close grain,
and the hackberries open their crowns.
Her mother is now buried on the hill
she chose, where the Shawnee were before,
the place only entered from the east, off
the river, as if the morning sun.

As the wings of the elms, the inner parts
of the earth roll in tremors of the fault,
and the silver mass of the river
is lead weight. In time Clark signs away

the land grant of de Carondelet,
lying, and being between the River Saint Cosme
and Cape Girardeau, and bounded on the east
by the Mississippi, and westwardly by White Water.

Her mother, Charlotte Pemanpieh Bougainville,
was *the natural daughter of Louis Antoine,*
who went around the world. A plant
bears his name, an island, and straits,

but her father chose other verses
for her mother's stone: how she followed nature
and was perfect for it.

Find these lines carved in Latin
in Missouri marble, consort to the sky.

KARL TARO GREENFELD

The Great Leader

W E WILL COME LIKE bad weather, a storm of dust and hoofbeats and steel, of carbines firing skyward, of war cries and horse breath and clanging boots in stirrups and rattling equine teeth chomping bits. We will envelop the desert and then the farms and then the towns and at last your cities, a wave, a pestilence, a plague, a swarm, a flood, a stampede, an infestation, an engulfing, an overwhelming, a great rolling up and twisting of the earth so that pouring down upon you is fire and stone and bone and entrails. We are thousands, tens of thousands, beyond the horizon, a horde to overwhelm your paltry fortifications, your flimsy defense, your delicate skirt of propriety, your garter of modesty, your undergarments of shame. We are massing, growing with every second stronger while you weaken; we are gathering, becoming ever more confident while your doubts redouble; we are expanding, our chests heaving full from deep, engorging breaths, our arms and shoulders thickening with hard, unbending muscle while you diminish and atrophy, your breathing labored, your lungs rattling, your arms splindling.

We have ten squadrons on horse for every squad you have on foot, a dozen warriors in the saddle for every one of your boys cowering in a hole, and our women! Our women produce ten strong sons for every one spawned by your decadent, pallid, malnourished city whores. Our aim with rifle and bow is true to five hundred meters, our curved swords deadly swung from our mounts, our mailed fists ready to reach down from on horseback to wring you by your bean-pole neck. We will come at dawn, we will come at dusk, we will come by day and by night, over mountains, desert, prairie, and ice, up rivers, boring tunnels through the earth, an advance of thousands that will trample every square meter of your pathetic little state.

We will slaughter your cats, eat your dogs, and burn your crop. We will use your houses for kindling, your thatch for fodder, your furniture for bayonet practice.

We will shit in your mouths. We will piss on your faces. We will rape your wives and shoot our seed into your daughters. We will wipe our cocks on your holiest books.

We will march you from your city and we will kill every man, we will impregnate every woman, and we will enslave all of your children. We will rip up every one of your cobblestoned streets. We will tear down your churches. We will quarter your machines, your engines and generators, our stallions pulling them apart and our smiths forging them into blades that we will use to castrate your sons. We will imprison your leaders and slice off their pricks and parade them through our encampment with their own genitals shoved into their mouths. Our hunting dogs will grow fat from drinking human blood. Our warriors will grow weary from cutting necks. Our children will grow tired from whipping your children.

Our Great Leader will lead us into battle.

We all recalled him from previous campaigns: thick-legged, sturdy-hipped, barrel-chested, brawny-armed with a pronounced chin, sharp cheekbones, and long, flowing, thick black hair, he was the embodiment of the best traits of our horde: strong, brave, fearless, a gifted rider, a sure shot, a quick blade. He was not only our Great Leader, he was our best warrior.

He was said to have been studying the arts of war in preparation for this campaign, to have become as wise as he is valiant. With the Great Leader in the van, we will be invincible.

Soon, very soon, we will come.

We encamped in the great mountains intersecting the lesser range that ran northward into the State. We were thousands now, restive, our horses running out of forage and our warriors growing thirsty for blood. We knew you were weak. Your defenses barely manned, your troops raw and undisciplined. We had sent squadrons through the desert, had made sport of pillaging your southernmost villages. We were sure you were soft on the outside and hollow in the middle. Unleash the horde, we begged our commanders, who instead of blowing the great battle horns and ordering the war drumming, were poring over maps and charts in their campaign tents.

What were they worrying over? We would sweep before us any resistance. Every one of you we had captured had proven to be weak and decadent. You were children; we were warriors. Our Great Leader, surely he understood this. But he had yet to arrive. Perhaps he was waiting for even more squadrons to gather from even more distant tribes. The sacking of the capital was not an event to be missed, we all knew, and we all planned to become rich from our spoils.

Our camp lay on a broad plain between peaks, beyond the sight of the most southerly of the State's fortifications. At night perhaps you could see our fires, as we could see yours, but by day we were invisible. We were growing impatient, had spent a month playing polo with sheep's heads and fighting with wooden practice swords. We were ready, had been ready for seasons, yet still the commanders dawdled, the Great Leader did not appear.

We were a great horde, yet as we waited a fortnight, there was among us a slow-spreading concern. Were we losing our focus? Our ruthlessness? It was hard staying battle ready day after day, waking to await the call to arms, the clarion for attack, only to realize by midafternoon that there would be no war that day. And then doubts set in: Did the Great Leader not trust us? Was the enemy stronger than we thought? And what about rumors of secret weapons, of flying machines and armored automobiles, of cannons that could shoot flame? We had dismissed them, yet as we tarried, we began increasingly to speculate: Could a horseman at full gallop with a lance run through the armor of a metal-clad automobile? Would a muslin facewrap protect from poison gas? Could an airship drop stones that would topple a horse?

The Great Leader would know these things.

The tribes had been gathered for a month. We were tired of eating only horse-meat and mare's milk porridge. We needed everything: women, liquor, water— oh, what we would have given for an apple or apricot. We were supposed to be bivouacked here temporarily, a way station on our way to plunder, yet somehow we had become stuck. Our boredom made us benumbed, sluggish. We grew rest-less waiting for the fight, we grew so restless we fought each other, we grew so bored with fighting each other we grew even more restless. It should have been simple enough, we grumbled, a hitching of saddles, a mounting up, a setting forth, and then the great horsewave would move north in a hurricane of dust. Yet each morning passed with no more urgency than the collective desire of each man to find a place to piss in the prairie without stepping on another man's feces.

The camp was ankle-deep with our waste, with horse dung and human shit and the palm leaves we used to wrap mare's cheese, the charred wood, the ash, the balls of horsehair, the bits of straw and oat, and everywhere, the dried and aerated manure, blowing up around us in steady, soft, hot gusts.

How long would we stay here? How long could we stay here? An army grows stale as sure as any bread, grows weary of being weary, loses edge and eagerness to fight. We were being bled of our will as surely as if we were actually bled.

When, oh when would the battle be joined? Where was our Great Leader?

The Great Leader finally appeared borne on a tented palanquin, a vast, square platform the length of four men a side, carried on the shoulders of twenty slaves, each holding a protruding beam. The palanquin moved slowly, unevenly. We were all surprised the Great Leader did not come by horse. But when we saw him emerge from his conveyance, we understood immediately: he had grown immense, so obese he could not longer mount a horse without crushing the poor beast. He wore a red, pink, and brown robe, a campaign tent's worth of fabric draped from his shoulders like a tarp over a statue. Pointy yellow slippers capped his impossibly tiny feet. We speculated that it was an act of exceeding dexterity on his part to stay upright and not teeter to one side or the other. It would have been faster and easier for everyone if he had simply lain down and allowed his attendants to roll him from the palanquin to campaign headquarters.

He had once led daring and ruthless raids against the State, interdicting rail lines, looting villages, ransoming officials. But now, it was hard to imagine him in the van of a column, requiring, as he did, this huge, unwieldy form of transport. He walked in slow, unsteady steps, his immense head tilted down, careful to measure the trail ahead lest a pebble or twig unsteady and topple him. His face was red from exertion, his thick, black beard springing in wiry tufts from his swollen red cheeks. He wore some sort of blackish mascara around his eyes, an affectation of his tribe, but the ink was running in black rivulets that joined his beard and gave his whole face below the eyes the appearance of a man trapped in a thick spider web. His crown, the heavy silver-and-gold tiara passed down from great horse leader to great horse leader, perched precariously atop his unkempt tangle of graying black hair, the crown designed a hundred years ago for a much smaller man.

The thought among all of us was: This is our Great Leader? This is the warrior king who will lead us into battle against the powerful State to the north? This is the mighty horseman whose very name inspired men to tremble and women to faint? He certainly had the girth of an entire horde, but did he have our loyalty?

Yes! we reasserted. Yes, we would follow him anywhere. He merely had to give us the command and into battle we would ride.

Our Great Leader lumbered up the wooden ramp and into his campaign palace,

143

a series of intersecting circular tents all affixed to a great tent mounted on a center pole twenty meters high with lion and horse sigil flying on pennants. Preceding him into that tent, in the days before his appearance, had been a bounty of wine, fruit, slaughtered and dried meat and a seraglio of dwarves, clubfoots, hermaphrodites, and dog boys. And finally came a stream of consultants and experts in the art of war, hired by the Great Leader from the finest and highest institutions of martial learning.

Would we really follow him?

Yes! Yes, we would.

A few years ago, the Great Leader had introduced the missionary sexual position to our society, and now he was experimenting with other imported ideas. It was announced that the Great Leader had been studying the ways of the modern State to the north and felt there was much to learn from these half-men.

We were told that the Great Leader was reviewing our battle formations, our war plans, and had proclaimed that we were living in a new era, that our old methods of raid and pillage were no longer the norms of modern combat. There were, he said, rules of engagement, a decorum of the battlefield, a method and system to warfare that must be observed by both parties; otherwise, the ensuing battle would be chaos.

We couldn't simply ride into the State's territory and rape and kill everything in our path—that was the old way of warfare, the Great Leader announced. The new way, the modern way, taught to him by consultants he had hired for the task, was to dismount, line up in orderly columns, with our shortest warriors in the front and our tallest in the back, and then march toward the enemy position, firing our carbines and launching our arrows when we were within range.

We were perplexed by this set of instructions. For one thing, most of us struggled to shoot or fire from a standing position; we were only comfortable on horseback. And for another, since when had the great horsewave, the great southern horde, ever directly engaged the enemy? Our method was to bypass the enemy position and fall upon him from behind or at dusk or even at night. But no, the Great Leader's consultants explained, the important thing, the honorable thing, was to defeat the enemy army on the field, and so win a clear and decisive victory, measured by tallying the corpses after the cessation of fighting.

We were confused.

*   *   *

War was inevitable, as ineluctable as the rising of the sun or the falling of night. We must go to war with the State; our relative strengths required it. They were ebbing, we were gaining, our conquest the logical result of this imbalance. This was how antagonistic cultures and races behaved: we shied from a fight when both sides were too equal. If one was stronger, as we were now, that equilibrium no longer held. When the State was strong, they pushed us south. Now we were strong and would push them north.

That was what brought the Great Leader here, to the center of the horde, to take command of the great horsewave that would wash over the State. And it was time to unleash the horde, we all agreed; our horses had grazed the pasture down to dust, our own foraging was returning nothing but nettles. We were already slaughtering spare mounts for meat.

The retraining was proceeding too slowly. Long meetings at which the consultants, wearing the jackets and buttons and decorations of uniformed, professional soldiers, would describe to us, sometimes with the aid of charts and maps they had made and mounted on easels, the techniques and methods of the campaign ahead. They gave us documents on which we were to answer a series of multiple-choice questions. They assured us that these "examinations" were simply to gather information about how much we knew about war making, and to identify areas where we might need improvement. They promised we were not being graded.

They explained to us that in modern battle, the best 10% of soldiers would perform well and be promoted to higher rank, the next 20% would survive, and the remaining 70% would either be dead or wounded. Our goal, the consultants explained, was to be among that top 10%, or at least in the top 30%. We should not, under any circumstances, settle for being in the bottom 70%.

The stark numbers gave us all pause. Was that true? Seven out of ten of us would be killed or maimed in the battle ahead? That put war in such a negative light. They were taking the fun out of it. At night, around our campfires, we would discuss what the consultants had been teaching us, their demonstrations of the proper posture to maintain during the advance—chin high, expression stern, chest thrown back, a confident stance wider than our shoulders, "the body language of victory," we were told. And when we were shot, we were supposed to fall forward to lie facedown on the earth. That would make the tallying easier.

Meanwhile, the Great Leader remained ensconced in the splendor of his campaign tent, and in the evening, we could hear the lutes and zithers, the lotars, the chime of bell necklaces and bracelets affixed to the necks and hips of slave boys.

We endured his noisy entertainments, the laughter and grumbling and even the cacophonous farting of his courtiers, the high-pitched giggling of his eunuchs, the raised toasts of his consultants.

Our creeping sense of doubt about our prospects concerned us. For a horde, more than anything, must be confident, must be sure it will trample any opposition, must ride with brimming and unassailable swagger lest it pause before any of the many obstacles a horde may face. There were, the consultants reminded us daily, many obstacles. There were natural obstacles—rivers, mountains, deserts, and storms—and those thrown up by the enemy—the circular guns, the artillery, the trenches, the soldiers—and each of these the consultants continually and warily explained, belaboring the risks we faced. The consultants said our horde's advantage was in numbers. We outnumbered our enemy and therefore could afford to lose numerous engagements and still, after all the blood was shed, be a respectable horde. We were, they explained, like a school of fish or flock of sparrows; individual fish or birds would be constantly picked off and killed, but the whole body of organisms, the school, the flock, or, in our case, the horde, would survive. The strategy was, they explained, to use this numerical superiority to wear down the State, so that the horde would eventually prevail, though many of us would die before that happened. They showed us a diagram of how this would work, our horde represented by a lozenge shape, continually shrinking as it moved up north into the State. We were shown chart after chart, until finally the shriveled, tiny-but-still-lozenge-shaped horde arrived in the capital. Well, any horde would lose some enthusiasm when every day it was reminded of how perilous the very life of each individual hordesman was. We had never really thought in these terms before. We had never really thought about anything before, if we are being totally honest here. That had been one of the great pleasures of being a hordesman, that freedom from doubt and self-appraisal. We took great risks precisely because we didn't know they were great risks. If we had known, well . . .

Now some of us were becoming concerned about myriad issues related to the impending invasion. Not least the timing! There would soon be crops to be harvested, mares to be stitched, stallions to be gelded, goats to be slaughtered. This whole invasion was supposed to be wrapping up by now yet here we were, still mired in complicated preparations. When we complained about this scheduling conflict, we were told by the consultants that these preparations might seem wasteful but once we were actually in battle we would be grateful. When we asked which battles they had actually fought, they admitted they hadn't actually, themselves, fought in any battles. They were usually on to their next campaign before the armies they had prepared went to war, such was the lot of the mercenary consultant. But they also explained that very few commanders had ever implemented their recommendations to the extent that our Great Leader was planning to do, which excited them greatly. Usually, they lamented, their suggestions were filed away in some campaign desk or officer's bureau and forgotten.

We would be a great test horde, they said, a great case study in the theories of warfare, brought to life! We would go down in history!

In the night, we heard horses saddled and swords, spears, and bows sheathed as some of our colleagues began to steal back to their families and yurts. Every morning, we would wake up to find fewer and fewer of our colleagues. Our horde was shrinking, our perceived numerical superiority dissipating. The consultants said this was normal, that all armies suffered from attrition. And the horde was noncompulsory. We warriors were summoned by the Great Leader, and we could either show up or stay home. It was strictly our choice. Those who didn't join the horde felt a certain shame or embarrassment, and that peer pressure was usually enough to sway every able-bodied man to the horsewave. We were now, however, experiencing the downside of those casual terms of service. A man could, if he so chose, take his horses and go home. And with the consultants still explaining their plans and the Great Leader debauching in his tent, our horde's loyalty was diminished.

This wasn't the great, thrilling invasion we had been promised. We hadn't killed anyone. There hadn't been a single rape. No booty at all. War was supposed to be fun, we reminded the consultants, who disagreed, insisting that war is serious business.

The change in the weather, the dry heat giving way to damp, thick air, augured the late summer rains. Soon, the steppes would be mud, a quagmire unsuited to our horsewave. The consultants shrugged at our warnings of the impending season change. It was clear their plans made no provision for atmospheric conditions.

If we attacked in the rain, how would be set the fires that would so terrify the villagers, how would our horses make pace, how would we forage? The invasion would be a slower, more drawn-out affair. We asked the consultants: what about winter coats? We were prepared for the usual spring/summer campaign. This would be an autumn offensive, one that required, obviously, a different wardrobe. Again, the consultants had not factored this into their planning.

The camp was filthy, the hordesmen sluggish, the horses ropy and thin and dull-eyed. The greatest horde in history reduced to men biding time between dysentery bouts.

The Great Leader appeared, shirtless, his vast, hairy chest and stomach descending from his neck, layer upon layer of fat rolling over his belt, a cascading waterfall of hairy, human gut, his girth such that he looked like he could have swallowed a man whole. He still had his beard, and was now dusted with some kind of gold powdering so that his face shone in patches. Sweat dripped from his forehead, cutting rivulets into the gold coloring and causing gold to be smeared into his beard, as if he had just consumed a particularly messy dish of brightly colored food. He took his place outside the flaps of his campaign tent, beneath our standards and an intricate tarp of interlocked, vertical horses, held up over him for shade by six of his courtiers.

He announced he was there to address our concerns. Our Great Leader had a curious voice, soft and airy, thick with mucous and saliva so that if you were near him you could hear the strands of esophageal fluids separating as he spoke. He paused frequently, searched for words, making a great effort to sound eloquent and articulate when what we wanted, what we expected, were the usual shouts and cries of bloodlust and havoc. The Great Leader was supposed to remind us of our destiny, the horde's destiny: to kill, to pillage, to dismember and burn and grind human bones to dust. He was to pound the earth with his spear, then slaughter prisoners with a great ax and hold up their severed heads and promise us more, more, more. That's what the Great Leaders used to do.

But this Great Leader expressed a desire to address the recent complaints about the invasion process and the delays in implementing the consultants' recommendations. He wanted to kill as much as any of us, he reminded us, but we all had to adhere to the new process. It was better than the old process, more efficient, easier to measure, and scalable: it would work if we had a small horde or a large horde.

This was progress! he explained. And soon, very soon, we would be killing and raping and looting in an orderly and organized manner—

Then an archer's bolt, hissing through the air, found his eye socket. He continued speaking for a moment, promising victory, before he stopped, blinked with his one remaining eye and reached up with his chubby hand and felt the shaft of the arrow that had penetrated his skull. He looked around, as if checking his vision, turned to see his courtiers and then back to the horde, trying to ascertain what was different now.

He paled, opened his mouth soundlessly. Seeming to either understand the severity of his wound or to actually be dying, he swayed, and while we stood in silence, fascinated by this spectacle of our Great Leader's assassination, he pitched forward, falling on his face and driving the arrow completely through his skull.

There, that *was* easy to count: one dead Great Leader.

The men of the horde were silent. When it was clear the Great Leader was dead, we wandered back to our tents. We gathered our bedding and cooking pots, our spare clothes and our good-luck talismans, we took up our armor, our robes, our guns and our swords and our bows and our arrows, we painted our faces and we brushed our horses and fed them what grain we had left.

We barely noticed when the consultants departed the camp—with the Great Leader dead there was no one to pay them. We paid little heed when the Great Leader's courtiers and minions and freaks and harlots were raped and butchered by our fellow hordesmen. We sent out riders to those who had returned to their families.

We were silent as we made our preparations, the traditional preparations that our fathers had made and their fathers before them.

We were silent as we went to war.

CARRIE SHIPERS

Fidelis

Because watchdogs failed to warn Rome of the attacking Gauls in 380 BC,
each year dogs were ritually crucified near the temple of Iuventus.

They know when they've been chosen. They cower
and cry, lick or bite the hands that grab their scruffs
and drag them to the cross. Mostly we take strays,

though we always need a pet or two—clean, collared,
well fed—to show that justice rules us all. Their paws,
held still for nail and mallet, smell like grass, like dew

and rising bread. If the watchdogs had done their job,
signaled *stranger* and *attack*, we'd be spared our task,
pity we feel but have to hide. Men may scream or faint,

but most await their deaths with glazed acceptance.
Unless we crack their skulls or cut their throats to make
them quiet, dogs howl and whimper to the end. What must

they think of us, their source of food and shelter turned
to beasts more vicious than themselves? Is knowledge
of the watchdogs' failure, bodies on the cross, passed

from bitch to pup, within a pack or household? We know
what dogs deserve, but not how much they understand
of sin, punishment, payment for betrayal.

Confession

When you aren't sure what to write about, write about something
you can't tell your mother.
—UNKNOWN

I stopped calling for no reason because
you didn't always seem glad to hear from me.
Last week, my dog got more medical care
than I did during my entire childhood,
and he wasn't even sick. I don't talk
to my brother because he's an angry drunk.
When I was a teenager, I lied a lot
more often than I got caught. I hardly ever
wash my sheets or save the greeting cards
you send for Halloween or Groundhog Day.
Your coffee makes my stomach hurt.
I have friends whose advice I actually follow.
I can never tell that you've lost weight,
don't always trust you'll take my side.
When you say you're worried about me,
I feel like I've done something wrong.
I knew I was moving to Wisconsin
for months before I told you. Because
I'll never be ready to live without you,
I have to practice while you're still alive.

SUSAN BLACKWELL RAMSEY

A Story of Small Subversions

aqua regia: a highly corrosive mixture of acids capable of dissolving the
noble metals, such as gold, silver, and platinum

You know that story about the King of Denmark
and all his subjects wearing the yellow star
the Nazis tried to force on Danish Jews?
Never happened. The Nazis promised Denmark
self-government if they didn't fight back,
never forced yellow stars on anyone. What is true

is that after the Swedish Academy
gave a jailed dissident the Nobel medal,
Hitler prohibited any German,
Jew or not, from having one. Besides,
a third of a pound of 23-karat gold
would certainly be confiscated. So
George de Hevesy, Hungarian Jew
and chemist, took the medals of his friends
the physicists von Laue and Franck, dissolved them
in aqua regia, shelved the flask among
dozens of others and escaped to Sweden.
After the war he found his laboratory
undisturbed, precipitated out the gold,
and gave it to the Academy,
who recast the medals and reawarded them.
                                        And so I ask

what makes this is such a satisfying story?
No lives were saved, no grand examples set.
A story of small subversions. And yet. And yet

I love wit hiding treasure in plain sight,
defying guns and muscles with learning, love
the blend of spite, affection. And besides,
it's the story for which we all yearn,
the one where evil's beaten by smart and good,
the one where everything we've lost returns.

But wait, there's more. In 1993
a wave of hate crimes ripped Billings, Montana—
Jewish graves defaced and rocks thrown through
windows displaying menorahs. The editor
of the newspaper remembered how King Christian
and all the Danes put on the yellow star.
So the paper ran a full-page picture
of a menorah, and all over Billings
people remembered something that never happened,
and lived up to it, putting them in their windows.
There were more rocks, a bit more vitriol,
but in the end it worked. It seems that courage,
like any noble metal, can be dissolved
but also can be precipitated out
and make a story true—whether it happened or not.

IAN BASSINGTHWAIGHTE

The Elephant Walk

IT WAS IN THE FOOTHILLS of northern Thailand that Noi first learned elephants were better swimmers than fish. She was nine and thought they were tanks, or buildings, or horses that ate too much butter.

"They're practically submarines," said Ajaan Yo, a man like her father even though he wasn't. "Go to the river and look if you don't believe me. You will see ten trunks poking upward for air; there are giant creatures under the surface, and they are swimming."

Noi was afraid of the elephants because even the small ones dwarfed her by a factor of twenty. She kept her distance from them. Even the old ones. Even the blind one, who was calmest, who moved around the fields, proceeding slowly, collecting his food.

"Go touch one," said Ajaan Yo.

"What if it steps on me?" she asked.

"That's not their purpose."

"But there are accidents."

He named her Noi-Tao, which meant "little turtle," the day he found her sitting by the moat in Chiang Mai, the old part of town that used to be walled. It was halfway through the monsoon. The sky opened every afternoon and dropped its burden for the trees to drink. She was sitting there, in the rain, which collected in her hair and her clothing and even in her skin, like she had stopped being a girl and started being a sponge. She was younger then, hardly eight.

Ajaan Yo sat down next to her and asked if she had an umbrella, if she was cold, and whether she'd eaten that day, but she bit him and tried to steal his wallet.

The heat came in March and the elephants spent all their time in the water. Noi liked to stand in the grass and watch them swim, which meant what she really did was count trunks and wonder how deep the river was. It was thick and brown

154

like soup, so she couldn't see what the elephants were doing beneath. Maybe they weren't swimming at all. They could've been doing anything. Dancing, racing, wrestling in the underwater mud.

Sometimes she threw in a stick to see if an elephant would throw it back. But the stick would buoy on the surface, then disappear downstream.

Ajaan Yo opened the rehabilitation center one year after an elephant sat on his leg. The center was land and the river on it. There was a giant hill in the far parts that seemed more like a mountain if you were climbing it and sweating. The property was acres and acres and acres of shit that was no good for farming. There were no fences. Just this place he called the Valley even though it wasn't one.

He left Bangkok when he was young and his skin was lighter. He moved north, where the rice got sticky and the mangoes got sweet. But he didn't go for the food. He went for the opium, for the dense land it grew on, and for all the money he thought he could make selling bulk highs.

People called it the Golden Triangle. Only when he arrived, there was no gold left for him. He ended up working the fields instead of owning them, which had been the ambition. To leave home, which wasn't a family, not really, just a mother obsessed with the study of Buddhist sutras, who meditated more than she ate.

An older man with a hammer and a whip sat on top of a fat black beast. The man was called a mahout, the driver, the one who steered the elephant like it was a bus. Like there was no heart in its chest, just an engine that turned rhythmically. The man shouted "Nam!" which was the beast's name, and meant "water." Water was a good name because that's what a river is and a river never rests. The mahout whipped Nam's skin but Nam didn't move any faster. Instead, Nam dropped the log she carried in her trunk. The mahout whipped again, and again, then hit Nam hard on the skull with his hammer. Nam screamed like elephants do. She walked slowly in a circle. She waved her ears. She screamed again, louder. Her muscles tightened and her eyes got wide.

The old man shouted to Ajaan Yo: "Boy! I lost my spike. Throw another! Boy! Quick! Why are you waiting?"

Ajaan Yo learned about the spikes the day he started logging. (He cut the wood and the animals moved it.) That first day at noon, when the sun was hot, a drunk worker talked in between spoonfuls of white rice: "If you work many years they will let you ride the elephant. You will be the driver. You will make more money and you will work less. But don't think it is so easy! The elephant may go crazy, you never know when. If it does, the elephant will throw you. You will fall and you will lose your breath. Try running. Try to stand up and run. Try finding a tree the elephant won't kick over. Good luck hiding behind it. The animal will find you. It will use its trunk, which looks flimsy only when those fat beasts sneeze or are scooping water, and it will grab your leg and pull you into the air and you will dangle and the beast will stare you in the eyes. I have heard that sometimes the really angry ones, those ones are a darker color, something about their blood is different—they whisper things. But you are dangling by the leg and you are seeing the world upside down and you think all of it will end soon and then it does. The elephant will slam you onto the ground and you will lose all of your air and maybe your back will break, but it doesn't matter because the elephant will put its foot on your chest. The elephant will press down slowly and, you know, they weigh more than a bus."

Ajaan Yo ate his rice, too. He stared at the field and the trees at the far end of it. Then the man continued: "There is a soft spot on the elephant's skull, right in the middle where the plates meet. You put the spike there. When the elephant spins, when it screams, when it is about to shake, you hammer twice. Once for the bone and once more for the brain beneath it. I saw it happen my first year. The elephant found its anger and the mahout found his fear. Then his hammer, which he swung. It sounded like the man was making something out of wood, bang-bang, then the elephant fell back into the grass and died in the sitting position."

Noi played at the water's edge. She threw rocks instead of sticks, aiming not for the gray trunks directly, but near them. The goal was to lob each stone precisely so that it would hit the water, sink, and rest on the back of an elephant, which would be under the surface doing whatever it was doing, maybe building something or kissing another elephant it loved. When the stone landed, the animal would feel something tickle its skin. It would think there was a fish nibbling, maybe the fish had mistaken the elephant for a piece of food. That would be a good reason for an elephant to laugh and it would do so. That laugh would make bubbles and when those bubbles hit the surface, Noi would know her trick had worked. She would know there were bodies attached to those trunks.

She threw stones and watched. Then she threw more stones and stared more at the water. No bubbles came so she tried a stick again, but it floated away. Then she threw a flower, which she thought was very smart of her. Flowers were so beautiful and the elephants would be stupid if they didn't come to the surface to smell and maybe eat one.

But the flower had no weight and there was no wind to carry it. When she threw the plant, it didn't hit the current and was eddied back to shore.

Noi wasn't born, she was hauled out of her mother legs first through a hole in the woman's stomach. The day it happened: a doctor with a very fine knife sterilized the mother's torso with iodine, then said a prayer in his head like he always did. Steady-my-hand, et cetera. Then he carved her from sternum to below the navel and pulled the baby out in a rush before the mother's blood pressure tanked and she turned purple.

Staff congratulated the doctor on saving the baby even though he wished he could've saved more. The mother, whose face was mangled when the car rolled. Her son, the little one in the backseat, who would've been Noi's pesky but protective older brother had he lived even a few hours more. It wasn't the impact that took him. It was the belt, in which he was tangled. When the ambulance arrived, the car was still sideways and he was still hanging upside down, kind of flying.

Noi was an only child when she was born and an orphan a few minutes later. She was premature and couldn't breathe or cry. A machine pumped air into her lungs and a tube fed her. Slowly she grew, and the Thai government tried to find her a home. But she was passed around because nobody wanted a girl. A girl was a mouth to feed and body that would never be good for farming.

A bamboo steamer sat between them. Ajaan Yo pulled the lid off and Noi put her hand in the rice.

"It's hot," said Ajaan Yo.

Noi handled the rice quickly and shoved it into her mouth. Her face turned red before she spit the ball onto her plate. Then she touched it again and burned her fingers before she found enough patience to wait.

"You've been here a year now," said Ajaan Yo. "Today it's a year."

"That's almost like a birthday!" said Noi, who didn't know the date of her own.

"Then it's a good thing I brought a gift."

"What is it?" she asked. She stood up. She forgot her hunger. She forgot everything and began to shake.

He stood up, too, then leaned against a stick and hopped to the cupboard. He pulled out a book of pictures and gave it to her. It was the whole world in two dimensions. Photographs of cities. And mountains with snow on them. And weird animals she'd never seen before, like frogs the size of pin tips. It was many pages and all of them were colored.

Ajaan Yo sat down to eat again and Noi sat with him, flipping through her book. With every page she said, "What's that?" and, "Can we go there?" and when she got to the end she asked if there were more pages hidden somewhere else. When Ajaan Yo said no, that's all there is, books don't go forever, she cried and he hugged her. Then she opened the book again and started over.

The old man shouted to Ajaan Yo: "Boy! I lost my spike. Throw another! Boy! Quick! Why are you waiting?"

The elephant spun. Her ears flapped and her anger grew and her skin got blacker.

Ajaan Yo pulled a spike out of his bag. But he didn't know how to approach an animal that was the size of a bus. He needed to be closer. Ajaan Yo needed to throw the spike accurately, probably underhand so the mahout could catch it at the top of its arc, just as the metal was about to fall again, when it was moving slowest, almost floating.

"Throw it!" is what the mahout shouted, so Ajaan Yo ran close, as if that was his only purpose, and tossed the metal like it was fragile. The mahout caught the spike and placed it on the elephant's skull, against which it looked more like a nail.

Bang, and the elephant spun again, screamed, and took one step backward toward Ajaan Yo, who stared like elephants couldn't trample men in reverse.

Bang, and the beast went quiet. Then she slouched a bit, as if beginning to sit. Ajaan Yo kept watching because it felt like a movie or a painting of some kind. But gravity took over and the beast fell back. Ajaan Yo dove but his leg was trapped, and he, too, started screaming.

"Where do elephants come from?" asked Noi.

"They drop into the forest when it rains too hard," said Ajaan Yo.

"But that's far and they would die from falling!"

"Elephants are rubbery, fat, and good at bouncing."

"Not all of them are fat," said Noi. "Like that one. Maybe he hit the ground and got flatter?"

She pointed to the field, where Kung was walking. He was the blind one, the one who moved slowly and was always collecting grass. *Kung* meant "shrimp" even though he was at least a million times bigger than one. Still, his proportions were off. He was less round and more rectangular. The hair on his belly was long and the skin there was loose.

Ajaan Yo stood, hopped, and fetched the rest of the chicken from the wok. He returned and they both ate like it was a race. But it wasn't hunger that moved them. It was the sweetness of the mango peels in which everything was cooked. It wasn't meat anymore. It was almost fruit.

They finished eating and sat on their own beds, which were mats under mosquito nets. She played with a flashlight and shined all the elephants in the yard while he whistled and waited for her to sleep.

When Noi was very young she was fostered by a woman who was good at loving. The woman was called Khanom Jeen, which was a kind of noodle. She took Noi to the Chiang Mai Zoo. Khanom Jeen wasn't rich, but she wanted her child—that is how she thought of Noi, as her own in all the ways that mattered—to see the weird things the world made.

They visited the panda family first and watched the little ones wrestle. Afterward they visited the bears, the black ones. There was a lazy one in the corner who rested on his back and stared upward at a sky that was blue and contained no clouds, or water, or sun really because you could look up at it without squinting. Noi stared at the bear for almost an hour. When the bear growled, Noi approached the fence and growled back. Then Khanom Jeen tried to pull her along to see the snakes and the flowers they hid in, but Noi just gripped the bars and growled again.

How many men does it take to tip a dead elephant, balanced upright in the grass? Sitting there. Sitting quietly. Praying almost, with her eyes closed. Seven, it turned out. Seven men and a rope.

They pulled, the elephant tipped, and Ajaan Yo's crushed leg went free. He didn't move. He was blacked out, not even dreaming, just pure black in his head. He woke up later in a hospital he didn't recognize with an envelope full of cash and a note in his pocket that said, "Don't come back, don't tell anyone what happened, not the police, we will kill you, here is money, it will pay for your leg."

He was luckier than most. The landowner didn't ask the muscle to shoot him dead and leave him there for the trees to eat. Maybe the landlord, who had so much to lose, all this information, didn't do it because it wasn't Ajaan Yo's fault. Not exactly. Not fully, at least. Sure, Ajaan Yo was a burden now. A loose end that could squeak to the police about production. But he'd tossed a spike and saved a driver's life, and the forest was where karma mattered most.

It didn't take Noi long to discover a pattern in her various parents. They wore guilt first and looked heavy as they searched for ways to remove her from their lives. Maybe she was too expensive and too quiet and would be too ugly to marry even when she was older and fatter in the right places. But they wouldn't say that, not out loud. The father would then focus on his cigarettes and start coughing, would say he needed medicine, and the mother would yell like there was no money, it was either food or medicine, there wasn't enough for both, even with the government subsidy.

That would happen, or something like it, and days later the tone would change. Guilt would give way to distance when they admitted their love was too much responsibility. They would call the government and the government would say there was no place for her. Still the parents would insist she wasn't right for them and a small truck would eventually take her somewhere new.

Noi cried the first time it happened. Then each time after she stole something out of the house instead and carried it with her. Every bit she took became a recollection that never changed and lived on in her pocket. There was a pendant, and an old coin, and a wrinkled picture of the king.

So when Khanom Jeen got hot and spent her days in bed sweating, Noi grabbed her sandals and ran away because this time she didn't have to be told: Noodle Mom didn't want her anymore. On her way out, Noi tried but failed to steal something bigger. It was one of the cats.

In the middle of the night, when the bugs were spinning in the air, or dancing, or looking for little bits to eat, and the buzz of them was thick, Noi sat up and said, "Ajaan? Are you still there?"

"I'm right here."

He turned on his flashlight and pointed it at himself so she could see him, and he made a funny face.

"Are you awake?" she asked.

"I think so."

"How do you know the elephants don't want to step on me?"

"We sleep here every night," he said. "We are in this box of cinder blocks and wood and if they really wanted to step on us they would come in here and do it."

She turned on her flashlight and pointed it toward the field like that would keep the animals away.

Ajaan Yo said, "Don't worry. That isn't their purpose, remember? I told you."

"But how do you know?"

"I spend some time talking with them, especially the fatter ones, reminding them to please not sit on me. They stay quiet except for their breathing, like they've never looked at me even once and thought, There is a chair."

The doctor said amputation was best because the bones didn't break under the weight of whatever crushed them. That wasn't the right word, breaking. They fell apart and flattened.

Ajaan Yo shook his head like, *What?*

"Crush syndrome. That is what is happening now; look at your leg, it is fat and filled with fluid, literally a gallon or more. Your body is trying to recirculate all the protein, potassium, and acid the muscles in your leg released. All those dying cells. It's not just a damaged limb anymore. Your blood is diluted and we're fighting anemia."

Ajaan Yo shook his head again, like, *These words have no meaning.*

"There's more. With crush syndrome there is always more. Kidney failure is next. All the stuff in your blood, all that potassium and other debris, it clogs you. Your kidneys could die. You're on dialysis. That tube, there? That's dialysis. What comes next? That is always the question. Heart failure, maybe. That's also from the potassium. But the acid, too. It messes with your blood pH and that makes the heart beat funny. And if that heart gets tired it might quit, you just never know."

"Take the leg; I don't care," said Ajaan Yo. "I will walk with a stick."

They gassed him and he went pure black again. There was nothing inside him, not even a dream.

Noi found the longest string she could, then tied one end to a stick and the other to a hook. She put a worm on the hook, walked to the river, and threw that worm into the water. While waiting for an elephant to bite, she considered how hard it would be to pull the elephant to shore and what exactly she would say to it on arrival.

Who taught you to swim and would they teach me?

You might be taller than me but I know how to read.

We can take a walk together if you promise not to step on me.

But no elephants nibbled at her bait, so she screamed at them.

"Come out of the water! You are one hundred times bigger than me; why are you afraid?"

"Why doesn't Kung go swimming?" asked Noi.

"He can't see underwater."

"But he's blind!"

"That's true."

"What happened to him?" she asked.

"A farmer raked his eyes out when he got too old to work. The farmer was going to shoot Kung afterward because he was just a big animal to feed, this thing that might knock over his fences."

"Did Kung run away? He got lost and wandered here accidentally, like I did!"

She laughed at all the ways she was exactly like an elephant, then lifted her arm to her face and made a loud sound like her nose was actually a horn. She fell over from laughing too hard and hit her arm on the cement floor, which made her quiet while deciding if she was too old to cry over things like that.

Ajaan Yo said, "I brought him here, traded a bicycle and a bag of mangoes for his saggy skin. I got the better deal, I think. I can love mangoes all I want but they will never love me back. With Kung it is different. I touch his trunk and he kisses me."

Surgery was followed by an infection and a drug haze, during which Ajaan Yo asked if his leg would grow back. He said his knee hurt and the doctor said, "You don't even have a knee, not the one you're pointing to anyway; it's gone now." Still, it ached and Ajaan Yo tried to touch it even though the whole thing was missing. It was in a biohazard bin or burning in a furnace.

"Crush syndrome!" said the doctor. "I told you there is always more. There's infection now and that means your blood is sick. I told you that at the beginning. There's so many things we still need to fix."

* * *

"Where did the rest of the elephants come from?" asked Noi. "I know they didn't come from the rain."

"It took years, but I collected them. They're all damaged in some way. Mam, the really fat one that is always spitting water, she was hit by a bus; that is why she is very slow. Kluay carried too many logs in his trunk and that is why it dangles there. He can't use it anymore to pull grass so the others feed him—have you noticed that?"

"Where did the land come from?"

"No one wanted it; there's nothing here. It was cheap and wide and perfect."

"Do you have a mom? You never talk about her. I have been here for more than a year now and I want to know."

"I have a bunch of fat gray friends and a very small daughter."

Noi tried hard to forgive all the elephants that wouldn't come out of the water, but it didn't work so she got madder.

She stood on the shore and yelled to them. "You are not allowed to swim so much, you are not fish, you were not made that way, you were made for the forest!" Then, "Please come out!" Then, "I don't want to walk through the trees by myself. Ajaan can't go because he only has one leg and a stick, but all of you have four legs and a giant trunk for balance. You will never trip!"

Nothing happened so she picked up rocks and aimed for the trunks directly, but missed. Then she turned around with the intention of stomping homeward, to her mat with a mosquito net draped over it like a tent, where she would sit and think of new ways to lure them out of the water.

Kung was standing there and Noi's face turned pink because she stopped breathing. Kung walked over to where the trees started and Noi followed him at a distance that felt safe.

"Please don't sit on Ajaan," said Noi. "I would miss him."

Kung just sneezed, then kicked over a tree and ate it.

Noi moved closer than she ever had before and put her hand on his trunk.

Alligators

How at the VFW bar, he rolled up his sleeves. Alligators curled around his wrists. *Eighteen of them*, he said. *I just like them, I don't know why.*

How I saw one in the yard and told my ex-wife, *Don't go out there now.*

How an alligator slides backward into its pond the way a ruined man slides into himself.

He fought off six of them with a pool cue. *One of them cut me right here with a goddamn broken bottle.*

An alligator slept on his forearm. One curled around his neck.

How their bellies flatten the grass they move through so you can follow their trails, how they sleep at the pond's edge, hundreds of them along the shore—

Should of known. They come up behind you when you ain't expecting it, hit you on the head with a beer bottle. And for what?

He was halfway drunk, his good eye focused on the row of bottles below the TV set.

I only laughed to keep him quiet.

I'd lost my job a few times recently, my wife was in Connecticut somewhere with my kid, and outside it was nighttime, cicadas lighting up the air with their racket.

You will maybe find arms or legs in its belly.

You will maybe find scratches around its eyes where she tried to fight it off.

You be good now, you hear? You drive safe. You watch your back. You hear?

Sometimes, one comes out at night and crawls along the sidewalks or stalks through the lawn. Sometimes, they're in the swimming pool or your garage, sometimes they're in your living room drinking, they're in your kitchen waving around a broken beer bottle sometimes—

At first I couldn't find my keys. Then I couldn't unlock the door.

In the dark water, the black hearts keep beating.

Cleveland, Ohio

The last thing my father did was lie in bed.

A machine kept beeping. It stood by his feet and its screen glowed greenly.

The falling snow looked like insects swarming around the streetlamps.

I was afraid to turn on the light.

His hands had swollen and when he breathed, the liquid in his chest grew thick so the room filled with the sound of it and no one came,

the nurses wouldn't drain his lungs, wouldn't hold his hand or cut him open, the nurses stood in the doorway and shook their heads and smiled,

said, *He's asleep, he can't feel a thing*, and increased his dose

while far away the phone rang and rang and the sky above Cleveland filled with insects

and the machine at the foot of the bed considered my father

who was sleeping and would go on sleeping forever.

+

Years later, a dog had been barking happily all evening,

and now it was past midnight and the BI-LO glowed dimly behind the apartment buildings.

Someone had chained him to a post and he greeted the passing train, the buses that rumbled down West Twenty-Fifth Street, that man walking toward the intersection who stopped as if to pet him, then, under the red light, aimed carefully and shot him in the head.

The dog whimpered

long past the time when the man turned the corner and the light turned green,

and from his balcony my neighbor tilted his bottle to the evening, said, *Finally!* and went inside for the night.

+

When he inhaled, I heard a sucking sound, followed by the long rattle of his exhalation

and across the hall a woman with her back to me held a child and sang all night

and whether the intravenous tubes extended into her or into her child I could not tell

and every room was bathed by the televisions and the green light of those machines awake at the ends of the beds

until I looked out the window and into the snow where years later a man would shoot a dog at the intersection of West Twenty-Fifth Street and Jay Avenue.

+

The dog was still whimpering, its legs twitching, and when I reached through the fence to pat him

he tapped his tail happily against the grass

and when I walked away, he whimpered, so I returned and it took that dog half an hour to die.

+

He is still barking into the very same night my father sleeps in now,

having made death, at least, a thing to be slipped into quietly and recalled as breathing

that slows and rattles as the nurse says, *He is dreaming, he is comfortable, it won't be long*, and increases his dose

and I cannot know if he is dreaming or merely emptied,

and that woman wrapped in tubes holds her child and sings

and Cleveland spreads out around us, the Terminal Tower's cold lights, the glowing green arrows up Carnegie Avenue, and the red arrows,

Shaker Heights, Beachwood Place buried in snow, the mall like a great machine blinking along the highway's edge.

THOMAS REITER

Releasing a Tree

Softly pummeled overnight, the lower
limbs of our Norway spruce
flexed and the deepening snow held them.
Windless sunlight now, so I go out
wearing hip waders and carrying
not a fly rod but a garden hoe. I begin
worrying the snow for the holdfast
of a branch that's so far down
a wren's nest floats above it like a buoy.
I work the hoe, not chopping but cradling,
then pull straight up. A current of air
as the needles loft their burden
over my head. Those grace notes
of the snowfall, crystals giving off
copper, green, rose—watching them
I stumble over a branch, go down
and my gloves fill with snow. Ah, I find
my father here: I remember as a child
how flames touched my hand the time
I added wood to the stove in our ice-fishing
shanty, how he plunged that hand
through the hole into the river, teaching me
one kind of burning can ease another.
The branch bobs then tapers into place
and composes itself, looking
unchanged though all summer
it will bring up this day from underfoot.

Exposures

Often for Mathew Brady, lying ill and sleepless
on his pauper's cot, it's 1862 again
and New Yorkers by the thousands are attending
his gallery exhibit *The Dead of Antietam.*
Many weep, giving names to the fallen.
The fingers of the dead are swollen, arched
and spread like those of pianists: God's music,
he believes. He hears a man saying to himself,
"For my enemy is dead, a man divine as myself is dead."
Some ask if these scraps of paper around their sons
could be letters home. Did he collect any
before the wind could carry them away?

After the war the nation tried to heal itself
by forgetting Brady's work. Creditors seized
his darkroom wagons, cameras, and glass negatives,
ten thousand exposures taken by the dozen assistants
he directed like a general from First Manassas
to Petersburg. Who knows me now, thirty years
after Appomattox? he asks himself,
unable any longer to feel bitterness.

His wife Juliette so loved the calla lily,
its cuplike swirl of white inflorescence,
that every year on the anniversary of her death
he has come to this same Manhattan greenhouse
and carried one home in its clay pot to set
beside their bed. But now the single flower
will rest on his nightstand in a charity ward.

A man carries a square of glass from a barrel
to the wall of the greenhouse where yesterday's

hailstorm shattered panes. What he sets in place
is a photographer's glass negative. Closer,
and Mathew Brady sees it's May 4, 1864,
the day before the Battle of the Wilderness.
A group of the 2nd Wisconsin Infantry
is playing cards, writing letters, smoking clay pipes.

All but one young volunteer stay motionless
for the thirty seconds of exposure.
A pipe smoker, his smile almost a smirk,
he exhales in puffs like smoke signals
that in the developing solution become
a blur, the negative's shadow pouring
from his mouth—as though, Brady remembers
thinking, I've captured an exorcism.

On an assault field you're hurled from one thought
to another quick as a musket ball
can ricochet, the pipe smoker told him
before the battle. Ah, his name was William,
Brady remembers. Then you're on your belly,
time and motion stop and you're studying a fossil
tossed up by the shell that might have killed you.
The workman reaches into his barrel.

Bearing a calla lily, Mathew Brady passes
through light streaming through the dead
in the thickets of the Wilderness.
Is William there? he wonders. All those years
of working in darkness could have come to worse,
it strikes this dying man so he almost laughs aloud,
than to be found in a greenhouse gallery,
which is no house divided against itself.
Here Federals and Confederates alike
are called upon to force the flowers.

In Praise of Lichens

We're out walking a path in silence,
carefully looking away from
each other and into the trees, having just
broken off an argument
before one of us could say something

that couldn't be turned back from.
You stop, then I follow you to an oak
it must have taken lightning to split
down the middle like that,
the halves falling away from each other.

Now the sapwood and heartwood
are a common for lichens, these
pioneer plants that do not flower.
On the light air currents we make
as we look closely, spores rise

to further colonize the forest.
Here's a lichen that reminds me of
my grandpa's beard, tobacco stained,
and then another that with its
intersecting lines and blank spaces

looks like a map. We're right . . . here.
Warming to our game,
you counter with what could be
the open mouth of a baby bird,
and flaring near it an orange corona

you dub TJ2011 in Andromeda,
the newest supernova in that galaxy.
It's time to go back, but look:
in shadow among the flourishers
here's something we nearly missed.

Let the end of all fallen trees
be our bending together like this
over a lichen it takes
both of us to read. I see it
as an alien craft's dish antenna

locked on Mars in '50s sci-fi. Yes,
and you add how those beings
attacked by fighter planes and tanks
only wanted to teach us earthlings
how to love one another.

FORTHCOMING SPRING 2013

the Southern Review

POETRY

Gilbert Allen, Nicky Beer, David Bottoms, Robert Cording, Carol Ann Davis,
Ron De Maris, Ghalib translations by M. Shahid Alam, Margaret Gibson,
Anna Journey, David Kirby, Joy Ladin, Laurence Lieberman, Alison Pelegrin,
David Petruzelli, Alexandra Teague, Corey Van Landingham, Laura Van Prooyen,
Ross White, David Wojahn, Jake Adam York

FICTION

James Lee Burke, Chip Cheek, Jaquira Díaz, Tamas Dobozy,
Mika Seifert

NONFICTION

Bonnie Jo Campbell, Kirk Curnutt

ART

dioramas by Lori Nix

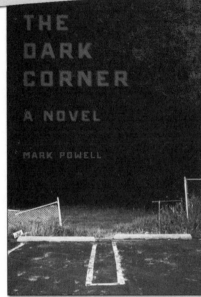
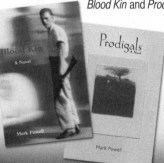

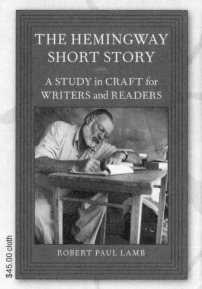
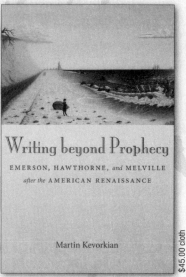
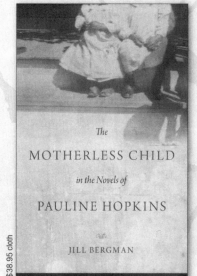

27ᵀᴴ ANNUAL TENNESSEE WILLIAMS / NEW ORLEANS LITERARY FESTIVAL
March 20–24, 2013 • tennesseewilliams.net

For a complete schedule of events and ticket information visit:
www.tennesseewilliams.net or call 504.581.1144

Writers and readers, take note:
Book your passage to New Orleans March 20-24, 2013 for a five-day feast of literature, theater, food, and music in the French Quarter's Hotel Monteleone! Come hear award-winning writers and artists, join in the illuminating conversations and master classes, delight in our late night literary surprises, and sign up for the raucous fun of the Stanley and Stella Shouting Contest.

Stellar! Just a partial line-up includes:
Douglas Brinkley, Maureen Corrigan, Michael Cunningham, Danielle Evans, Dwight Garner, Silas House, Emily Mann, Ayana Mathis, Don Murray, Marsha Norman, Leonard Pitts, John Shelton Reed, Nathaniel Rich, John Patrick Shanley, Amy Stolls, John Jeremiah Sullivan, Zachary Lazar, and many more.

Most of the events take place in New Orleans' historic French Quarter.
Festival Headquarters: The **Hotel Monteleone**, 214 Royal Street

"Make voyages! Attempt them... there's nothing else." —Tennessee Williams

Poe and the Remapping of
Antebellum Print Culture

Edited by J. Gerald Kennedy and Jerome McGann

$45.00 cloth

"In *Poe and the Remapping of Antebellum Print Culture,* J. Gerald Kennedy and
Jerome McGann have pulled together an impressive collection of essays
that seek to extend, revise, and challenge the insights produced by a decade
of scholarship on nineteenth-century U.S. print culture."

—Meredith L. McGill, author of *American Literature and the Culture of
Reprinting, 1834–1853*